Sexy After Cancer

MEETING YOUR INNER APHRODITE ON
THE BREAST CANCER JOURNEY

Published by Sexy After Cancer LLC and SAC Publishing

Copyright © 2012 Barbara Musser

Sexy After Cancer, 765 Woodland Trace Ln., Cordova, TN 38018

For information, visit us at **www.sexyaftercancer.com** or contact us at info@sexyafterancer.com.

Library of Congress Control Number: 2012903927

ISBN# 978-1-4675-1660-0

Musser, Barbara

Sexy After Cancer ~ Meeting Your Inner Aphrodite on the Breast Cancer Journey

Editorial assistance: Karen Frank, www.linguisticalchemist.com

Cover design: Sandee Whalen, SINC Communications

E and print book design: Ana Hillis, Repurpose for Profit

We Have Come to Be Danced used with permission of Jewel Mathieson

Female Pelvic Floor Anatomy© drawing used with permission of Amy Stein, MPT., Author of *Heal Pelvic Pain*

Cover Artwork "Journey" by Ani Rose Whaleswan, oils on cardboard 2003, Living Stones, unlimited

For Jenner Rose

My Miracle Angel Girl

I love you, Honey!

CONTENTS

PREFACE

Sexy After Cancer is an expression of my vision and passion for helping women and their loved ones on the breast cancer journey. The book contains advice and information relating to health, emotional, psychological, sexual and spiritual care. It is not intended to replace medical or psychotherapeutic advice and should be used to supplement rather than replace regular care by your doctors or mental health professional. It is recommended that you seek your physician's advice before embarking on any medical program or treatment. All efforts have been made to assure the accuracy of the information contained in this book as of the date of publication. The author disclaims liability for any medical or psychological outcomes that may occur as a result of applying the methods suggested in this book.

Barbara Musser

Barbara Musser

FOREWORD

When I was first told I had breast cancer in 1989, my first thought wasn't that I was facing my mortality. My first thought was that I would lose my breast and be less desirable as a woman. I had a good friend who had a mastectomy 25 years before I did and I had seen her scar. I thought it wasn't pretty.

I did have a mastectomy, and because I had no health insurance at the time, I couldn't afford reconstruction. When I eventually did get health insurance, I was told I couldn't have reconstruction because the area had been radiated. So I learned to love my new body and accept the scar as my badge of courage. Reading Ronnie Kaye's book, *Spinning Straw into Gold*, helped.

I wish I would have had the resources that Barbara is providing in this book, to help me through that difficult transition. But what I have learned is that this transition is ongoing. We continue to learn and evolve and it's never too late to influence that evolvement in a direction I want to go.

Barbara describes many of the changes a woman may be experiencing as a result of breast cancer and the treatments. Merely reading these descriptions may be comforting to some women. Without someone to talk to about her experiences, a woman might think she is the only one having them. Barbara normalizes them.

Acknowledging the changes and naming them is just the beginning. Barbara has included a buffet of practices and exercises, that can be done alone or with a partner, to help us move along a path toward healing and joy. Each reader can pick and choose which ones fit her needs the best right now. And she can come back later when she is ready for the next one.

Barbara has also included some education about what sex is and how the body/mind works that can be useful for any woman, whether she has had breast cancer or not. It's refreshing and empowering to have a frank discussion about this subject. It is a vitally important part of our lives, yet a very private part. Many of us are hungry for this level of information and assistance, presented in such a compassionate voice.

Thank you, Barbara, for opening up this conversation that so many of us have needed for so long.

Jan Adrian
Founder and Executive Director
Healing Journeys
www.healingjourneys.org

Barbara Musser

INTRODUCTION

This book is a gift to you from my heart and soul. It's a gift of love - to you and to myself. And it is a gift of gratitude for the journey of breast cancer.

I received my breast cancer diagnosis on my 37th birthday – I didn't know then that it would turn out to be one of the greatest gifts in my life. Since that time, for more than 23 years, I've been walking, sometimes crawling and sometimes running on this journey.

Along the way, I've supported many women – as a friend and companion; through teaching yoga, meditation and visualization. I became a sex educator, transformational workshop leader and healer – all of these helping to facilitate women in embracing and celebrating the experience of being women. I have also volunteered my time with many cancer support organizations. While the paths along my journey may seem diverse on the surface, together these experiences are why I call myself a "Doula for the Soul." Traditionally, a doula provides physical, emotional and informational support to women before, during and after childbirth. She recognizes the turning point in life that results from becoming a mother; understands the physiology of birth and the emotional needs of a woman giving birth; assists the woman and her partner in preparing for and carrying out their plans for the birth; stays by the woman's side throughout the entire labor; provides emotional support, physical comfort measures, an objective viewpoint and assistance to the woman in getting the information she needs to make good decisions; and she facilitates communication between the birthing mother, her partner and clinical care providers. She perceives her role as one who nurtures and protects the woman's memory of her birth experience. I perform similar functions as I help women and their loved ones to navigate the breast cancer journey.

Not long ago, I was driving a friend to surgery for a lumpectomy and she turned to me and said, "Barbara, I think this is your work, what you're doing with me, supporting me on my journey as a woman..." She planted a seed that has grown into a very large vision to help women and their loved ones as they navigate this journey. God was speaking to me through her. And I listened, and heard and saw a large vision to help women and their loved ones as they navigate this journey. It can be gnarly at times, frightening, confusing, a time for soul-searching and grit. There can even be moments of ridiculousness and hilarity alongside grace and magic. The range of experiences and emotions are as personal as each woman's own journey.

> in reality, sex is so much more than "haveing sex"

What I haven't seen, especially in my extensive cancer research, is much about the impact of breast cancer on one's experience as a woman, specifically as a sexual woman. You might be thinking, "This is NOT a time for feeling sexual. I don't even feel very feminine."

In reality, sex is so much more than "having sex." It relates to our self-esteem, how we see ourselves, whether we feel useful in the world, our sense of being empowered or feeling helpless. Our femininity and sexuality are the roots of our life force energy. This is the inner core of where we live, who we think we are and how we "be" in the world and this inner core is greatly impacted by the experience of breast cancer. Whether we love and feel comfortable in and with our body is the foundation for our experience of ourselves. If you feel betrayed by your body with breast cancer, it's hard to love and feel comfortable in your body.

Men define themselves through their sexuality overtly. For women, it's a subtler, but equally powerful force. The way we carry ourselves is an expression of our sexuality, as is the way we dress and even the way we speak. We live in a world that places a very high value on physical beauty and youth. Unfortunately, much of how we feel about ourselves is based on how our bodies look.

Our bodies are designed for sex, procreation and pleasure. The main function of our breasts is to feed our babies. Over time breasts have been sexualized and many women experience great physical and sexual pleasure through their breasts. So having our breasts changed or removed can have a large and very important impact on our sexuality and how we experience it and ourselves. Cancer can shatter our experience of our value, our beauty, our femininity and our sexuality.

If I lose my breast, or part of it, am I still a woman?
Will I still be desirable?
Will I or anyone else want to look at my breasts?

VI

These kinds of questions rise to the surface quickly and are often overlooked as we make treatment decisions and navigate the medical maze. We wonder who we really are and often our "shadow" comes out in full force, perhaps revealing parts of us that we haven't seen before. We keep a stiff upper lip and power through, dissolve into a puddle of despair and depression, or suffer in silence. Or we feel guilt, shame and embarrassment about being less of a woman and isolate ourselves in many ways. Or something in between happens for us as we cope with cancer and its treatments. None of these strategies helps us to heal, to become whole, to thrive.

will I still be desirable?

From there, it can be a rapid downward spiral into low self-esteem, feeling out of control and separate from your Self in fundamental ways. Breast cancer shakes us to our core and doesn't give easy clues for how to heal our heart, our soul or our mind. It's a time when many women dissociate from their bodies as a way of coping. Because of social and religious taboos, among other things, there are few places where we can talk honestly about our experiences, and even fewer where we can talk openly about the impact of breast cancer on our sensuality and sexuality.

I know that this is a very tender topic, not only for women with breast cancer, but for those who love us as well. How do we talk about this with our lovers, husbands or partners? Is it possible to have the experience of breast cancer bring us closer together and be a doorway into new and wonderful experiences of intimacy, love and sexuality? How do we heal and grow our relationships and ourselves?

That's how this book was born. To talk about the mysteries, challenges, delights and changes to our sexuality and feminimity that come with breast cancer. I'll share some of my own journey here, stories of others, interviews with experts and give practical tips and exercises to help you connect with your own radiant sexual energy as you heal your body, heart, mind and soul.

The book has 3 main sections which focus on:

- Inner work to build a foundation for healing, accepting, forgiving and loving your changed body

- Communication with yourself and your loved ones about intimacy and sexuality

- Intimacy and sexuality practices and exercises

There are many recordings of the meditations, visualizations, and some processes to make it easier for you. Please download them so that you can be guided by my voice and give yourself fully to the experience without having to think about what's next.

The focus of this book is primarily on your heart, your mind, your spirit and your body, specifically your sexuality. I may touch briefly on some medical information; however, this is not intended to give any kind of medical advice. Please consult with your medical caregivers for these issues.

My wish for you is that this journey is an awakening for you, awakening into your own power and magnificence, into loving yourself and your body. Here's to you, to your healing, your joy and your celebration of yourself as a beautiful, desirable sexual woman!

With great love,

Barbara Musser

WE HAVE COME TO BE DANCED

by Jewel Mathieson

We have come to be danced
Not the pretty dance
Not the pretty pretty, pick me, pick me dance
But the claw our way back into the belly
Of the sacred, sensual animal dance
The unhinged, unplugged, cat is out of its box dance
The holding the precious moment in the palms
Of our hands and feet dance.

We have come to be danced
Not the jiffy booby, shake your booty for him dance
But the wring the sadness from our skin dance
The blow the chip off our shoulder dance.
The slap the apology from our posture dance.
We have come to be danced
Not the monkey see, monkey do dance
One two dance like you
One two three, dance like me dance
But the grave robber, tomb stalker
Tearing scabs and scars open dance
The rub the rhythm raw against our soul dance.
We have come to be danced
Not the nice, invisible, self-conscious shuffle

But the matted hair flying, voodoo mama
Shaman shakin' ancient bones dance
The strip us from our casings, return our wings
Sharpen our claws and tongues dance
The shed dead cells and slip into
The luminous skin of love dance.
We have come to be danced
Not to hold our breath and wallow in the shallow
End of the floor dance
But the meeting of the trinity, the body, breath and beat dance
The shout hallelujah from the top of our thighs dance
The mother may I?
Yes you may take 10 giant leaps dance
The olly olly in free free free dance
The everyone can come to our heaven dance.

We have come to be danced
Where the kingdoms collide
In the cathedral of flesh
To burn back into the light
To unravel, to play, to fly, to pray
To root in skin sanctuary
We have come to be danced
We have come.

To see Jewel Mathieson saying this poem, go to this link:
http://tinyurl.com/6pulkjp

XI

FIRST, YOU CRY

Receiving a breast cancer diagnosis is transformational. In a heartbeat, your life changes and it will never be the same again. It's a physical, mental, emotional, spiritual, challenging, frightening and sometimes ironically poignant and funny journey through, with, over and around breast cancer.

To clarify: breast cancer isn't funny. Not at all. However, the journey? Sometimes things happen that are so ridiculous all you can do is laugh. The moments of lightness in what is sometimes a long and dark road, will help lift you up if you have the right attitude.

Breast cancer happens within the ecosystem of family, friends and community. So much of the journey is about how you respond to what's happening. There are choices in how you respond, in the midst of all the other choices and decisions you'll make. In this book, I will help you see that you get to choose how you react and how you experience your own journey.

My own diagnosis came in an odd way. I was married to a man 15 years my senior and he had severe heart disease. Through his research on treatment options, he discovered Dr. Dean Ornish's research project on reversing heart disease without drugs and surgery. He was fortunate to get into the treatment group of the study. I was invited to join as his spouse.

The group met twice weekly in San Francisco to walk, do yoga, meditate, visualize, share a meal and group therapy. I often walked with Don, a man with psychic gifts, who channeled other beings. One day while walking, a female voice came through him and said, to me, "Get your female parts checked out every 6 months for the next 2 years..." I thought, "psychic, schmychic..." but the seed was planted.

I made an appointment with my gynecologist, and the nurse detected a small lump in my left breast. I couldn't feel it, nor could she find it again easily. However, that began the process of detection, which included several mammograms, high magnification mammography, a fine needle aspiration biopsy and lumpectomy. The process went on for a few months.

Meanwhile, life went on. My husband and I separated and he eventually left the research project. I stayed, however, because they had become an important part of my life and felt like family. The tests continued, always with inconclusive results, until the pathology reports from the lumpectomy finally came in.

"You have breast cancer"

On my 37th birthday, I was on my way out the door to a meeting of the heart research group when the phone rang. It was the surgeon. Her very matter of fact cold and clinical voice said, "You have breast cancer." I didn't know what to ask or say, so I hung up the phone and went numb. I went into denial of the news immediately. I had no way to receive or understand this information.

I continued on in my state of denial and went to the meeting. When I arrived, I collapsed into a puddle of sobs and choked out the diagnosis. They held me and listened while I cried and rocked me as I sobbed. I was in shock and they simply cradled me in their love. No one tried to make me feel better, nor did they deny the news. The just sat with me and held me and loved me.

And then it was time to take action, to learn more and find out about treatment recommendations and options.

One group member, a physician, had volunteered to go with me to the meeting with the surgeon to discuss the pathology reports. She asked a lot of questions on my behalf and took notes because I was still in shock and I didn't know what questions to ask.

This is Rule Number One: don't go to any medical appointment alone. Always take someone with you so that they can gather information, take notes, provide emotional support and help you remember what you want to ask.

Regardless of the purpose of your appointment, you're likely to be faced with a new mountain of information, options and emotions at each one. Because of current managed care systems, you'll only have a short time with the doctor – perhaps as little as 30 minutes – and during this limited time you may receive a great deal of information delivered quickly by a doctor who sees patients just like you all day long. It can feel a bit like a factory!

Rule #1

Don't go to any medical appointment alone

Medical terminology is complicated and because doctors are exposed to the language and the realities of breast cancer every day, they can sometimes speak too quickly or sound cold and clinical, which doesn't help your emotions! You may spend much of the remaining time in your appointment dealing with your emotions.

The reality is that it's very easy to feel overwhelmed, get emotional or upset, and not be able to hear everything that's said, much less ask questions to clarify the information and recommendations.   Combine that with what can be surprising or upsetting news and you can understand why it's important to have someone with you during these appointments.   That said, you must be particular as to who you choose to accompany and support you.

Take someone you trust with you to appointments.

  ◦ How do you choose that person?

  ◦ What do you ask of them?

  ◦ How do you want them to act during appointments?

  ◦ Do you want them to help you make decisions?

Here are some things to think about and some possible criteria for making these choices

- If at all possible, assemble a team of 2 or 3 people who can fill this role. It's possible that one person may not be available for every appointment, especially if an appointment changes on short notice.

- If you have a partner, you may want to ask him or her to come with you. Remember that this may upset them as much as it does you, so they may be unable to absorb much information either.

- Think of people you know who can handle a lot of technical information and understand it and ask questions to clarify the information

- Can they stay on an even emotional keel if you get upset, angry or cry?

- Do they have any experience with breast cancer – their own, a friend or loved one?

- Do you trust them with sensitive and confidential information?

- Are they able to set aside their personal agenda and focus on you and your needs?

- Can they be responsive to your needs moment by moment, knowing that they may change quickly?

- Are they good at listening to hear and understand?

- Can they write legibly?

Before each appointment, talk with your companion about how you want to handle the appointment.

Write down any questions you have for your doctor.

- ⚬ Decide how you will introduce your companion to the doctor.

- ⚬ Do you want to do all the talking and have your companion take notes or record the conversation?

- ⚬ Do you want them to ask questions?

- ⚬ Do you want them to take their cues from you in each moment?

- ⚬ Do you want them to ask you if you need anything or have other questions to ask?

- ⚬ How do you want to receive their information after the appointment?

- ⚬ Do you want them to take you to a quiet place after the appointment so that you can express any emotions or talk about what happened during the appointment?

- ⚬ Do you want them to talk with your partner or children, if you have them?

As you go through different phases of your treatment and recovery, you'll have different needs. For example, you may need to do some research; you may want to talk with a dietitian or therapist; you may need to buy a wig or prosthesis. There are a lot of moving parts with treatment and your recovery.

It can be very helpful to assemble a healing team for this journey. Using the metaphor that you are the captain of the team, and the purpose of the team is to support you and your healing, think of what you might need as you go along.

Here are some things to think about

- ☉ In the beginning, you will probably be more involved with doctors than later on. So members of your team might include your surgeon, plastic surgeon, oncologist, anesthesiologist, and other medical professionals. Think of who they are for you and think of them as team members who work for you in your treatment and recovery.

- ☉ What will have you feel supported as you navigate this journey? Psychotherapy? Spiritual or religious guidance? Yoga, Tai Chi or other practices? Services and treatments that support the medical ones, such as acupuncture, chiropractic, Reiki, massage, and so on?

- ☉ During and after treatment, would it be helpful for you to talk with others on this breast cancer journey? Would a support group meet that need? What kind of group, facilitated or self-led? In a hospital or other setting? Small or large number of participants? Structured or spontaneous?

As you travel this path, your needs and interests will change. As that happens, change your team. You can eliminate and add whoever you want, whenever you want. The idea is to have you feel supported and that you have all the resources you need. You can even have gatherings of you and your team, for you to ask for what you need and want, feel seen and loved or do activities together. This can be as formal or informal as you want. You get to create this however you want.

One woman created a list of people that she wanted as her innermost circle. She invited them all personally to be part of a group that gathered monthly for a year. Each gathering included a pot luck dinner and time for her to check in with the group, update them on her treatment and experiences and outline her needs for the next few weeks (as far as she could predict them).

as you travel this path, your needs and interests will change

Next there was time for her to be held in the love of her circle and receive whatever she asked for, whether that was massage, spoken affirmations and appreciations, singing or chanting. She received whatever she felt that she needed and wanted for that evening. Her friends were all delighted to be part of the group and to support her.

A note about your needs during active treatment (post surgery, chemo and radiation): This is a time when many women need more help than they imagined. You may need assistance bathing and dressing yourself; with shopping, errands and meal preparation; with transporting the kids and help with homework. Many women find these times to be a roller coaster of feeling fine and feeling very fatigued and everything in between, plus the emotional and psychological roller coasters.   And needs can suddenly emerge or disappear.

There are some wonderful tools to help with these times: there are 2 websites (**http://www.caringbridge.org/** and **http://www.lotsahelpinghands.com/**). On both of these sites, you can set up your own private site within the site.   On your site, you invite friends and family to join so that they can receive updates, post notes, look at calendars and lists of what you need, and sign up to help.   They are very easy to set up.   I suggest that you have a friend serve as the administrator for you and you let them know what you need so that they can post it and the members can respond. This eliminates the need for lots of phone calls or emails to juggle schedules. The people in your circle want to help, and they especially appreciate knowing how to do that.   These sites make it easy for everyone to be informed and involved.

Some women find it helpful to keep a notebook or file that contains all their treatment notes, test results, notes from doctor appointments, resources and tips, brochures and medical bills, so that everything is in one place and can be managed more easily.

Here are some additional things to remember

- It's good to cry. Let the tears flow. You don't always have to be a big girl. Give yourself permission to feel all your feelings when they come. Know that tears on the outside are a sign of cleansing on the inside. Tears wash our soul clean. Tears can help to release tension.

  You don't always have to be a big girl

- Remember to breathe. When we're tense or scared, often the first thing we do is hold our breath. This only increases the tension and makes it harder to think and feel. I've included some breathing exercises at the end of this chapter.

- Surround yourself with people who love you, who will hug you when you need a hug, sit with you, hold you as you cry, just be there for and with you. Often we simply need to be listened to and have a container of love around us as we feel and express our feelings.

- If you don't have people to surround yourself with, seek out the following which, you may find through your nurse or hospital:

  o   Social Worker

  o   Chaplain

  o   Support Groups

Now is when you most need to take the best care of yourself. It is easy to forget to do that or how to do it. It might be helpful to you to brainstorm a list of what has you feel well loved and cared for, so that when you need it you have some things to do.

> Now is when you most need to take the best care of yourself

Here are some ideas

- ✿ Take a hot bubble bath

- ✿ Take a walk in a beautiful place

- ✿ Make yourself a pot of your favorite tea and serve yourself in a beautiful tea cup

- ✿ Pick or buy some fresh flowers, arrange them and put them in a place where you'll see them

- ✿ Take 5 deep breaths all the way into your belly, exhale slowly and repeat this phrase as a thought with each inhalation and exhalation: "I am loved."

- ✿ Buy or make a beautiful journal and write in it for a few minutes every day

- ✿ Give yourself a pedicure or manicure, or both

- ✿ Find a stuffed animal that comforts you and hold it while you sit or sleep

- Put on some music you love and move your body or dance

- Meditate or pray

- Call someone who loves you and who will just listen to whatever you have to say

- Go to a cosmetic or department store and have a free make-over

- Put on some beautiful earrings

- Take a nap in the middle of the day

- Write yourself a love note or leave yourself a love message on your voicemail

Tell yourself 3 things you love about you

- Tell yourself 3 things your love about you

- Get some exercise

- Call a friend who will just listen to you and let yourself empty out

- Watch a movie that makes you laugh

You have the opportunity to be transformed by this experience. Many, many people say cancer is a gift, even if it doesn't look or feel like it in the beginning. During my treatment, I kept a beautiful small gift-wrapped box on my altar to remind me of this great gift I had received.

Here's a one minute breathing technique to help you to relax and center yourself.

This is a very helpful technique to prepare you for this time.

Begin by sitting comfortably, so that your body is fully supported by the chair you're sitting in. As you sink into being supported, gently allow your eyes to close. Take a long, slow breath in, to a count of 7. Feel the air filling your brain, traveling down your spine, then around to fill up your belly and your heart. Then suspend the breath – neither breathing in nor out – for a count of 7. Feel your brain relaxing; relax your neck and shoulders. Then a long slow exhalation, again to a count of 7, exhaling completely. This exhalation glides into another inhalation, to a count of 7...

Repeat this 7-count breath 3 times. As you complete the third exhalation, let out a sound with the breath, if one wants to come out with the breath. ...

Allow your breathing to return to normal, with more consciousness and spaciousness and depth.

You can download a recording of this breathing practice here: **http://www.sexyaftercancer.com/bookmp3s/**

TRAVELING IN A FOREIGN COUNTRY WHERE YOU DON'T SPEAK THE LANGUAGE

Now that you know that you have breast cancer, there's a lot of pressure to make big decisions, fast. Decisions about treatment; timing and sequencing of treatment; researching the options and side effects; scheduling time off work; telling your family and friends; getting legal documents (see appendix) in order and so on. - all of this in the midst of the shock of the diagnosis.

Much of the emphasis in your decision making will be on the medical aspects of having breast cancer. Those decisions will have long-range consequences on the quality of many aspects of your life - present and future, including your body, your heart/emotions, your mind and psychological wellbeing, and your spirit.

This is a time when you need to think clearly and carefully. Considering all of the emotions you'll be dealing with – yours, and your loved ones, thinking clearly can be a challenge. Cancer is a scary word to many people and it can trigger big emotions. The last thing you need at this point is to have to take care of anyone but yourself. However, if you have children, you may have to do just that.

When you get your diagnosis, it's unlikely that you will be familiar with the terminology or procedures, most people aren't. Nor do we know about side effects or long-term effects of treatments. Fortunately with the Internet, there's plenty of information available and there are some wonderful websites and online resources to research. For some women, this is the easy part, and they dive into learning as much as they can as quickly as they can. For others, this kind of research is mind numbing. Get help if you need it.

As you research your options, you may also want to include other aspects of your care and take a more holistic approach to your treatment. There is a seemingly endless abundance of choices to make. Most providers are certain that their offering is the best way to go. How do you sort through all the information and know what's right for you?

Eek! This can feel like being dropped from the sky into completely unknown territory, where you have no map and don't know the language. And the pressure to make decisions quickly is strong. It can feel disorienting, strange, scary and way too fast.

First, stop and breathe. And breathe again. Know that you can take some time here for yourself. It's YOUR body and it's important that you make the decisions that you know are best for you. Only you can know this. I'm not suggesting anything other than honoring yourself and your right to make these very important choices.

This can feel like being dropped from the sky into completely unknown territory, where you have no map and don't know the language

When I got my diagnosis, I needed to get a second opinion. Actually, several second opinions. I needed to gather enough information so that I knew I was making the right choices for me. In that process I heard everything from, "You don't need any further treatment" to "Remove both breasts and ovaries and have chemotherapy" and everything in between. Not exactly comforting!

It was also very important to me to have a medical team who would work with me, not say that they were the ones making the decisions. I left several consults knowing that I had to keep looking until I found that. And I did.

This can be a very empowering time as you stand fully in the truth of your own wisdom and magnificence

Here's the bottom line: no one lives in your body but you. No one loves you like you do. Know that you can make whatever choices are best for you and that ultimately only you know what they are. Of course, get the advice and treatment recommendations of physicians you trust. Be aware, however, that they are trained in medical school to extend your life as long as possible, regardless of the quality of your life.

The challenge and opportunity here is to take responsibility for the choices you make about your treatment. I'm not talking about responsibility like an onerous burden; rather, the knowing that you are sovereign over you. This can be a very empowering time as you stand fully in the truth of your own wisdom and magnificence.

I recently accompanied a friend who will have a mastectomy soon to a consult with a plastic surgeon. The doctor talked about several different options for reconstruction. In the end, the doctor said that her objective was to have clothes look and fit well on my friend. There was no mention of my friend's emotions, the sensation she might lose or retain in her breasts, or about how she would look naked. These were all questions left unanswered by the physician, and which were an important part of her decision making process.

The medical professionals you see are highly skilled technicians; they are not trained to help with your heart, emotions or soul. They can advise you about pain management and will tell you what they think is the best treatment option from their vast clinical experience. The management of your emotional, psychological and spiritual health is left to you.

Ask questions during your consults and continue asking until you feel comfortable with the answers. Sometimes that takes more than one conversation. Remember not to go to appointments alone, but to take a member(s) of your healing team with you. Take time to discuss things before the appointment so that you both know what information you want to get. Record the conversations or have your healing team member take notes. This will help you as you digest and continue to gather information.

> *The management of your emotional, psychological and spiritual health is left to you*

Keep taking deep breaths. Being in this new land is a time when many women dissociate from their bodies, which is unhelpful at best in the long run.

Here are some additional practices to help you stay in your body and connected to yourself

1. **Energy Core.** Imagine a Core of universal energy that runs vertically through your entire body and connects you with heaven and earth. In Chinese medicine, we humans are known as the bridge between heaven and earth. Imagine this Core running through you and visualize it. What does it look and feel like to you? Feel the energy of heaven flowing down into and through you in this Core, and feel the energy of the earth flowing up into and through you through this Core. Feel it pulsating and vibrating with life and use it to anchor yourself in your body.

2. **Extending your roots into the ground.** Imagine that you have openings in the bottoms of your feet, and that you can instruct them to open so that you can pull down your energetic roots. Literally pull the roots like threads, out from the soles of your feet and extend them down into the earth. There is another root that extends out from the base of your tailbone. Feel that one coming down and extending into the earth. Use these roots to help you feel your connection to Mother Earth.

in Chinese medicine, we humans are known as the bridge between heaven and earth

3. **Joint mobility sequence.**

   ❻ Stand with your feet about hip-width apart, knees slightly bent, spine erect, shoulders relaxed

- Gently turn your head from side to side, looking first over your right shoulder, then your left. Repeat 5-6 times, then center your head

- Gently drop your chin toward your chest, and then lift it slightly back, only as far as feels comfortable. Repeat this 5-6 times, breathing deeply and slowly as you gently move your head

- Gently drop your right ear toward your right shoulder without raising your shoulder. Then drop your left ear toward your left shoulder without raising your shoulder. Repeat 5-6 times on each side, then center your head

- Roll both shoulders back and around in a big circle, 5-6 times. Then rotate and roll both shoulders forward and around in a big circle, 5-6 times.

- Extend your right arm straight out in front of you from the shoulder with your right thumb pointed up. Slowly raise your right arm toward the sky then rotate it back to make a big circle. At the top of the circle, rotate your hand so that the palm faces out and the thumb stays pointed up. Repeat 5-6 times, then switch directions and make the rotations in a forward direction. Then switch arms and repeat the sequence with the left arm, first backward, then forward

- Spread your feet wider than hip-width and rotate your hips in a big circle, first in a clockwise direction for 5-6 rotations, then in a counter-clockwise direction for 5-6 rotations

6 Bring your feet together, slightly bend your knees and rotate your knees first in a clockwise direction for 5-6 rotations, then in a counter-clockwise direction for 5-6 rotations. If you have knee problems or pain, do not do the rotations, simply rock the knees gently back and forth

6 Stand on your left foot and raise the right foot a few inches off the ground. Rotate the right ankle first in one direction for 5-6 rotations, then in the other direction for 5-6 rotations. Repeat with the other foot.

4. **Partner exercise.** Look into your companion's eyes until you feel reconnected with your body again. Sit or stand facing each other about 12-18 inches apart. Let your arms gently rest at your sides or hold hands with your partner. Gently look into each other's eyes and take a few slow, deep breaths. Continue looking into each other's eyes, feeling the connection between your hearts. Continue for 30-60 seconds.

5. **Bathing ritual.** Wash your hands and face and apply moisturizing lotion or cream. Use the ritual of bathing to help you feel your face and hands and come back into your body. As you apply the lotion or cream, apply it with as much love and tenderness as if you were applying it to the face and hands of your beloved, because you are.

THE FEAR FACTOR

Let's face it; cancer is a scary word, and a scary diagnosis. It's true that some people die as a result of having cancer. It's also true that many people live with cancer or are cured. There is no way to know what your journey with cancer will be. I'm not going to cite statistics because they are only numbers. You can easily research them if you're interested.

Breast cancer is often asymptomatic, just as mine was. We get called back after a routine mammogram for further testing, or we feel a lump during a breast self-exam and go see a doctor. These days with digital mammography, there are many more callbacks than just a few years ago. Getting the call to come in for further testing is frightening – don't go alone!

Waiting for test results can be excruciating. The mind can be quite a terrorist at such times. We are all deeply imprinted with a bias to look at what's wrong rather than what's right, or all that can go wrong. Many of us who were raised in the Judeo-Christian tradition have been taught the tenets of guilt and fear, and these currents run deeply through every aspect of our life.

there is no way to know what your journey with cancer will be

So here you are, having received sudden and frightening news, needing to make big decisions quickly, with no road map and not speaking the language. If we allow the fear to dominate, and it's hard not to, it's much more difficult. This is when it's important to know that we can choose our thoughts. We can't necessarily control our reaction as we get this news; however, we can control how we respond to the news and our reactions.

Don't
Believe
Everything
You
Think

What do I mean by this?

I'm talking about the mind set, which is our thoughts and beliefs. Studies show that the average person thinks about 60,000 thoughts a day, and that only 5-10% of those thoughts are conscious and chosen. The remaining 90-95% of thoughts are unconscious and automatic. These are based on the things we heard and saw as small children, before we had the ability to discern what was real and not. These thoughts are the basis for our belief systems, which is the lens through which we view life, ourselves and the world and

the average person thinks about 60,000 thoughts a day, and that only 5-10% of those thoughts are conscious and chosen

everything and everyone in it. Because the thoughts are so constant and automatic, we think that's just the way it is. We don't realize that we can work with our thoughts and manage them so that they are more supportive and take us in the directions we want to go.

Don't know what I'm talking about?

It's the inner voice in your head that is always giving a running commentary on everything. The voice that may be saying, "What voice?" The one that has an opinion about everything you say, do and think. The one saying, "Now look what you've gone and done...reading a book about controlling your mind. This is ridiculous..." or some variation on that theme.

it's like an internal radio station called K-FUK playing, all criticism all the time

I call these inner voices the inner bullies. Remember the bullies on the school playground? The ones who teased and taunted kids, made kids cry, had to be the kings and queens of the schoolyard? That's what the inner bullies do as well. They make us miserable, taunt and tease and judge us, and give constant criticism 24/7.

It's like an internal radio station called K-FUK playing, all criticism all the time. Sometimes it's VERY loud, especially at times when we're feeling scared or stressed.

What to do?

Change the channel by creating a new one. I like to call it K-LUV, the love station. Every time a critical, scary or judgmental thought comes up, consciously replace it with a loving message.   It can be as simple as, "I love you (your name)." Sounds corny, doesn't it? This practice is simple, but it's not so easy. Whatever your thoughts about it (which are the inner bully's thoughts most likely), this works. Think of it as a practice, like learning a new skill.   It takes a bit of time and a lot of repetition.   Remember when you learned the multiplication tables? It took a while, but you did it, and now you know them automatically.   It's   the   same   with cultivating more positive thoughts.

change the channel to K-LUV, the love station

Another way to deal with the inner bullies is to give them a job to do.   Assign them the task of finding things that inspire and delight you, rather than frighten you, for example.   Or have them find you a new friend. The idea is to give them a positive focus, which distracts them from tormenting you and also adds value to your life.

Here are some other tips for dealing with fear

◉ Give yourself an "Angel Shower." Just like taking a physical shower where the point is to get wet, in an Angel Shower, give yourself lots of positive messages. Soak them in without dodging them. One way I love to do this is to take a few pads of Post-It notes and write a little love message on each sheet. Then I put them up all over the house – on the bathroom mirror, inside drawers and cabinets, on my computer monitor, on the back door. I put them in so many places that I come across the notes all the time. I've also done this for friends as a birthday gift! When you see so many love notes, the messages get in and can help ease your mind.

◉ Listen to positive and uplifting recordings. I've turned my car into my transformation vehicle. Whenever I'm driving, instead of listening to the news, I listen to inspirational recordings. I have a library of positive teachings about how the mind works, the principles of love, the nature of creativity, and so on. There's an endless supply of these. I often trade positive uplifting messages with friends as well.

◉ Have a daily practice to focus your attention and mind on becoming aware of how your mind works. I've had various consciousness practices over the years, from yoga to meditation to prayer to visualization. There are many and they all work if used. The key is to find one that appeals to you, and then do it daily or regularly. It only takes 10 minutes a day to get good results. You'll be surprised at how quickly things can shift.

☉ Remember what you need to remember, when you need to remember it. This is great advice that I received from a therapist years ago. In times of stress or fear, it's easy to forget who we really are and what's most important. For me, it's knowing that I'm a precious child of God and that I'm here to bring more love to the world. This is very easy for me to forget when the chips are down. Guess what? These are some of the messages on my Post-It notes!

remember what you need to remember, when you need to remember it

4

FEELING LIKE DAMAGED GOODS?

Our culture places high value on physical beauty. Women's breasts have been a focus of this attraction to beauty for millennia. Many women have breast augmentation or reduction for cosmetic reasons, and good cleavage is a symbol of great sex appeal. Pinup calendars, Barbie dolls, bikini bathing suits, décolletage, push-up bras, and the list goes on and on. We can't escape our fascination with tits!

Breast cancer treatments can change the shape of breasts. Surgery, even a biopsy or lumpectomy, leaves scars or in the case of a mastectomy, we may have portions or all of a breast removed.

How does all this leave us feeling as desirable and attractive women? Do you wonder about this? I did. After my initial lumpectomy, I definitely felt misshapen and like damaged goods. I was single and certain that no man would want to be with me, now that I had a large red gash of a scar across the top left side of my left breast. I knew the days of wearing low cut clothing were over, and that I didn't want to be seen naked by anyone.

In 1990, I had the good fortune to participate in the "Love, Intimacy and Sexuality"

we can't escape our fascination with tits

workshops sponsored by the Human Awareness Institute. These workshops are clothing optional. That means that many people in the workshop are naked. Take a big breath... yep, naked.

At various times, participants have the opportunity to stand in front of the group to share their experience. Sweating and shaking, I mustered up my courage to do that because I wanted to be seen with my changed body and breasts. I stood there quaking in front of 80 men and women, naked, and talked about my shame and pain because of my disfigured breast. People smiled at me and sent me signals of compassion. Then I took a big risk and asked how many of them found me attractive, including my breasts. Almost every hand in the room went up, and many people said, "Scar? What scar?" I pointed to my scar. Several people smiled and said they couldn't see it, even sitting 6 feet away from me.

everyone in the room stood up and bowed to us to honor us

I was shocked! This was the beginning of my real healing. In that moment, the belief I had – that I was disfigured - was shattered and my experience of my cancer was reframed.

Later, many of the participants came up to me and told me how beautiful my breasts and I were, and asked if they could look, gently stroke or even kiss my breast. A few even knelt down and bowed, saying that this scar had saved my life. Several women came to me and said I had spoken for them, that they had also experienced breast cancer and didn't have the courage to do what I had done, and that I had done their work for them.

Later in the workshop, 6 of us stood in front of the group, all showing our surgically altered breasts. Everyone in the room stood up and bowed to us to honor us. There wasn't a dry eye in the house.

I knew that my beauty wasn't a function of what my breasts looked like

These experiences really helped me when I had additional surgeries to remove a large section of my breast and all the lymph nodes under my arm. Not only did I have additional scars, but my left breast was less than half the size of the other breast. Radiation therapy further altered the shape of my breast. Even though these were more radical surgeries than the initial lumpectomy, I was able to navigate with less concern about how attractive I was. Something had really shifted internally, and I knew that my beauty wasn't a function of what my breasts looked like.

A few years later I became a facilitator of these workshops and often spoke of my experiences with breast cancer. There were always women in attendance who identified with my story and carried the belief that they were "damaged goods" as a result of their cancer journey. I know that by facilitating these workshops and sharing my story, I helped many women (and men) heal the pain they carry about breast cancer and beauty and thinking they don't fit the "standard" for beauty in our culture.

5

FROM DAMAGED GOODS TO SELF ACCEPTANCE, SELF LOVE AND BEAUTIFUL

Since I had a partial mastectomy, my breasts are different sizes. I was offered neither reconstruction nor reduction of the larger breast. So I got a small prosthesis that fits in my bra, which makes my breasts look about the same size. And now I wear low cut clothing and love looking at my "girls." Because I'm comfortable in my own skin, love my body, and myself, I am often told how sexy I am. This has nothing to do with having had breast cancer, although that was a big catalyst for me to do the work I needed to do to accept and love my body as it is.

The Truth is that there is no such thing as "the" perfect breast. All breasts are perfect, each in their unique way, whether surgically altered or not.

The idea that we are somehow less than gorgeous because our breasts look different is simply not true. I've seen women who have beautiful tattoos where their breasts were previously and they are gorgeous.

If breast cancer has damaged your self-image, you can work on creating a positive view of yourself. Are you going to great lengths not to look at the scars on your chest? Your reluctance to face the scars is understandable. But it is important to get past this attitude.

Practices to love your body – whether you have a partner or not

There are several reasons for these practices. The first is simply for you to forgive, make peace with, and love your body. Second, they will prepare you and lead you toward feeling attractive and desirable, first with yourself and then with a partner or a potential partner.

Clothes cover

Fancy lingerie or nightwear may be the immediate solution to avoiding initial shock. If you want that protection, that camouflage, go for it. Indulge yourself. Plenty of women sleep with clothes on. Beneath clothing, a reconstructed breast or a good prosthesis looks "real" - it has the bounce, the weight, and the resilience of a natural breast. To a partner it feels very much like the real thing.

Responding to a discriminating market, many small shops offer an excellent variety of prostheses and cleverly adapted prosthesis pockets fitted into underclothing and swimsuits. Ask your local American Cancer Society chapter for a list of shops, or look in the Yellow Pages under Lingerie.

Even for the short term, while you're deciding whether or not to go ahead with reconstruction, a breast prosthesis may allow you to feel more comfortable about your image in clothes.

Easing into exposure

Beautiful lingerie can be your first step to getting into a pattern of relaxed sexual activity. (and remember you don't need a partner for sex!) Sooner or later you need to come to terms with the changes in how you look. It is important to accept your naked body, even if you never did before, and make peace with yourself. If you have a partner, you will need to let your partner look at you and come to a similar point of view. Take it little by little. This is easier for some than others. Some women find it freeing to walk around their room or apartment totally naked. One woman I know invited close friends over for dinner and when they had finished, she showed off her new reconstructed breasts, to "oohs" and "aahs" of approval!

The Final Step

The final step is to be totally naked (with your partner, if you have one). This seems to be the last stage in releasing the anxiety about your self-image. 'Cathy,' in a new relationship, finally worked up to letting her beau see her naked chest— and he applauded: "You really did something big, letting me see you. But I told you before, it wasn't going to matter to me."

'Ellen' said her husband's only concern was that she was alive, not whether or not her reconstructed breast was a match for the other. She says she was able to have a nipple-sparing mastectomy and the reconstruction looks fine, but she's more aware of the asymmetry of her breasts more now than before. She looks with a much more critical eye than her husband. As time passes, she's more and more able to accept how her breasts look now, and even to laugh at her scrutiny of her beauty.

> *Beauty is More Than Skin Deep*

With or without breast cancer, some women just don't enjoy being naked. You may need to face what you look like, but you don't have to force yourself into behavior that never suited you. Often, sex takes place in darkened rooms. When the lights are low and you're getting it on, whether you're totally naked or not, may not matter one bit.

What is beauty, and who says? The media and trends of the times we live in heavily influence us. As women, it's easy to succumb to the superficial definitions of beauty. I don't mean to demean physical beauty in any way. I'm talking about the beauty of the soul, the radiance that comes from standing in the Truth and Integrity of who you really are, which is a unique manifestation of divine consciousness.

> *What is beauty, and who says?*

Think of the women you admire and who you find striking or elegant or sexy. What is it about them that has you say that about them? What are the qualities? Usually what we're drawn to is either a reflection of who we are, or aspects of what we want to develop in ourselves.

Beauty has so many aspects:

A beautiful heart

Kindness and generosity of spirit

Speaking the Truth

Compassion for yourself and others

Being comfortable in our own skin

Knowing that we are beautiful

Practices to see your beauty

⚬ Every night before you go to sleep, tell yourself 3 things you love about you. Write them down in a beautiful journal.

⚬ Have a professional photo taken of you in an outfit you love. Put it in a beautiful frame in a place where you'll see it every day. Every time you look at the photo say, "I love you."

⚬ Look at yourself in the mirror as you brush your teeth, comb your hair, put on make-up and say, "You are beautiful."

YOUR BODY'S WISDOM

"Just wake me up when it's over... "

"This isn't the life I ordered..."

ound familiar? Any thoughts like this can be signs that you've dissociated from your body. Of course, that's natural if you don't feel like yourself. And with the treatments, it can feel like it's not you. I've talked with women who say they watched from the ceiling as they sat in the radiation or chemo room because it was all so surrealistic.

the best thing you can do is tune in to your body's wisdom

While these strategies may sound good, the best thing you can do is tune in to your body's wisdom. Developing the capacity to "be" in your body, all the way in, helps with the navigation. Really. This may sound counter-intuitive, and it really helps.

It's easy to feel betrayed by your body with a breast cancer diagnosis. For me, I had no symptoms, so the diagnosis came as a total surprise. Suddenly, my body, which had functioned beautifully, and still did, had cancer. How could that be? I made myself crazy trying to figure out why it happened to me, at the age of 37, with no history of breast cancer in my family, living a clean and healthy lifestyle, doing all the right stuff.

Cancer was a wake-up call for me. As I went along, I realized that I hadn't been loving my body or myself for a long time. I also realized that I regularly "left" my body and treated it less than respectfully.

> *I made myself crazy trying to figure out why it happened to me*

This was a big opportunity to make peace with myself and go deeper into loving my body. As I did this and reconnected with myself physically, I began to pay more attention to my body. Many of my old habits began to change. I lost my desire for caffeine because it made me jittery. My body wanted to move more, so I began to dance. I began to ask my body what it needed, and it answered! It wanted more rest, even better food, soothing creams and lotions for the radiation burn, more touch and sex.

Ways to tune in to your body's wisdom

◉ Yoga, Tai chi or other spiritual movement practices

◉ Dance – 5 Rhythms, partner dancing, or just plain moving to music

◉ Walk in beautiful places in nature

◉ Swimming

◉ Ask your body what it needs and write it in a journal

◉ Take naps when you need them

◉ If you want chocolate, eat it, some kinds are medicinal

Tip: Take 5 minutes a day and tune in to your body's wisdom, and then do what it says.

MIRROR, MIRROR ON THE WALL

Have you looked lovingly at your body in the mirror lately? Have you even looked at all? Some women stop using a mirror during and after treatments because they don't want to see themselves. This only causes more pain and separation from yourself. Would you do this to a friend? Would you avert your eyes to avoid looking at someone you love deeply because they are changed or different? Of course not, so please don't do it to yourself.

how we feel about ourselves, is what we project into the world Using the mirror as a healing tool is a powerful aid in coming to terms with yourself and making peace with your body. If you are not at peace with yourself, if you have not accepted yourself, it will be close to impossible for your partner to be at peace as well. Why? Because how we feel about ourselves, is what we project into the world, no matter how beautifully we dress or what we say.

By doing this practice with the mirror, you are changing the structure inside your brain and creating new neuronal pathways. Think of these pathways like grooves and your habits (including habitual thoughts) as the needle that follows those groves, like an old-fashioned vinyl record. All of our habits exist in these grooves, most of them created unconsciously. You can create new grooves or pathways consciously. The practice I am about to describe using a mirror is a conscious way to create pathways in your brain that support you. Research shows that it takes 30 days of consecutive repetition to create a new neuronal pathway.

you are changing the structure inside your brain

I call this Mirror Work, and it's a very powerful spiritual practice. It also works - really works.

Here's the format

There are 4 phases to this practice. Each phase lasts 30 days. Please follow the sequence given and do each phase for 30 consecutive days. After you have completed all 4 phases, you can repeat any phase that you want, in any order.

You'll need: a full-length mirror, a timer, box of tissues, a calendar to schedule and mark each day, optional soft background music and a journal for writing your experiences.

make this commitment to you - you are worth it

First, commit to doing this practice for 10 minutes each day for 30 consecutive days per phase. It takes a full 30 days consistently to make a lasting and effective change in your experience. Make this commitment to you – you are worth it!

Set aside 10 minutes daily to stand in front of the mirror. Doing the practice at the same time every day can make it easier. Think of it as a date with yourself. Set the timer for 10 minutes. Look into your eyes in the mirror and see what you see as you look into your eyes. Call on your compassion for yourself.

Phase 1: Dress up in your favorite clothes and stand in front of the mirror so that you can see your entire body. Look at your entire body with loving eyes and heart and then look into your eyes.

think of it as a date with yourself

As you look into your eyes, say out loud to yourself, "I love you (your name)." Continue to look into your eyes and notice any feelings that come up. Initially it may be thoughts like, "This is stupid" "Oh no I don't love me" "There's nothing lovable about me". Simply notice the thoughts, continue to look into your eyes, and say, "I love you (your name)." You can also say, "You are beautiful (your name)." Pick out three things that you like about yourself and say them out loud to yourself as you look into your eyes. Continue with these words until the timer rings. Take a few minutes and journal about your experiences – thoughts, feelings, anything.

Phase 2: Dress in lingerie and stand in front of the mirror so that you can see your entire body. Look at your entire body with loving eyes and heart and then look into your eyes.

As you look into your eyes, say out loud to yourself, "I love you, (your name). Your body is beautiful. You are a sexy and desirable woman." As in Phase 1, notice your thoughts and feelings, and continue to look into your eyes and repeat the messages about loving yourself and your beauty and desirability. Pick out three things that you like about your body and say them out loud to yourself as you look into your eyes. Continue until the timer rings. Journal about your experiences.

Phase 3: Stand naked in front of the mirror. Look at your entire body with loving eyes and heart, and then look into your eyes. Breathe deeply and use the breath to help you stay present if you need that. As you look into your eyes, say out loud to yourself, "I love you, (your name). You are beautiful inside and out. You are sexy and desirable." After each repetition, look at your entire body, breathing deeply. See your beauty and repeat the phrases.

After several repetitions, look at your breasts. Notice what you see as you look at yourself through the eyes of compassion. As you continue to look at yourself, say out loud to yourself, "You have beautiful breasts (your name)." Breathe and notice any thoughts and feelings that appear. Simply notice the thoughts and feelings, continue to look at your breasts and say out loud, "You have beautiful breasts (your name)." Pick out three things that you like about your body and breasts and say them out loud to yourself. Notice your thoughts and feelings, and continue breathing and repeating these phrases until the timer rings. Journal about your experiences.

pick out three things that you like about your body and breasts and say them out loud to yourself

Phase 4: Stand naked in front of the mirror. Look at your entire body with loving eyes and heart, and then look into your eyes. After a few deep breaths, look at your breasts and gently touch your breasts and scars, as if you knew that you were transmitting big love and healing energy right from your heart into your breasts.

You are. If it feels right to you, imagine that the hand of the Divine is touching you, bathing your breasts in Divine Love. Continue looking, touching and speaking, phrases like, "I love you" "You have beautiful breasts" "These scars saved my life" "My breasts are beautiful". "I am a beautiful, sexy and desirable woman." Pick out three things that you like about your breasts, your scars and how your body looks now and how your breasts feel and say them out loud to yourself. Continue until the timer rings. Journal about your experiences.

I am a beautiful, sexy and desirable woman

This practice is designed to bring up the unconscious beliefs, judgments and blocks to self-love and acceptance. In the beginning it may be difficult to be with yourself and feel any love for you. That's all our old unconscious programming coming up, and it's helpful to remember that those thoughts are not the Truth about who you really are. They are simply old beliefs, many of which you probably picked up before you had the ability to discern what supports you and what doesn't. Many people find it useful to say something like "thanks for sharing" to the unsupportive thoughts and then continue with the positive and loving words.

Note: Everything that is in the way of you experiencing love for yourself will rear its head. That's the point. Unless and until you confront the inner harshness, it's impossible to find self-love. That is why this practice may feel uncomfortable and sometimes intense. You may cry. You may feel angry or sad or afraid. Let whatever feelings arise, to arise. You may have difficulty looking into your eyes with love and kindness, or even looking into your eyes at all. 10 minutes may seem like 10 hours, so it's important to use the timer. Your commitment and willingness to engage with yourself at this level are the keys to breaking through the unconscious beliefs and judgments, the habitual thoughts that rule your life. If you do this practice as described, you will experience breakthroughs in your acceptance and love for yourself. 10 minutes a day for 30 days to deeply shift a lifetime of lack of love and judgment, is well worth it in my opinion. Try it and see what happens. You may be very surprised.

As you continue the practice, you'll notice that you will begin to believe what you are saying, and you will experience much deeper levels of loving you and your body and your breasts. There's no need to stop at 30 days, but you must do each phase for a minimum of 30 days. Make a mark each day on the calendar to keep track of the days. If you miss a day, you begin at Day One again. It must be done for 30 consecutive days to create the changes inside the brain, to create the new neuronal pathways. Your journal will reveal the inner shifts that are occurring.

> until you confront the inner harshness, it's impossible to find self-love

This practice is not for the faint of heart! It is very powerful, effective and works quickly. Being able to change your inner mental landscape in such a short span of time after a lifetime of judgmental thoughts is a miracle. Many of us don't think that we can change our thoughts, so we don't attempt it. Instead we are victimized by those Inner Bullies and think this is just the way life is meant to be. This practice, along with that of changing the inner station from K-FUK to K-LUV, will radically change your life and your experience of yourself.

FORGIVENESS

One of the shocks of a breast cancer diagnosis can be the feeling that life or your body has somehow betrayed you. It goes hand in hand with trying to figure out how you got cancer, especially if there's no history of it in your family. These issues can cause a sense of separation from yourself. The self-judgment and criticism that accompany this may bring up depression, bad feelings or fear. Any of these can slow down your healing and recovery processes.

Forgiveness can be very helpful. The place to begin is to understand what forgiveness is and what it's not. Forgiveness is not saying what happened is okay. It's not about forcing yourself to do anything. It's not about forgetting what happened. It's not about overstepping your personal boundaries or beliefs.

> *forgiveness is about letting go and releasing something that you're holding on to*

In essence, forgiveness is about letting go and releasing something that you're holding on to. It might be something someone else said or did to you that resulted in pain, anger or hurt. It can be something you said or did to yourself that has you judging yourself or feeling pain, anger or hurt.

I've heard it said that forgiveness is letting go of any hope for a better yesterday. We can't change what happened. What we can do is to go forward and not be constrained by what happened. There's no changing the diagnosis you received, nor can you return your body to its pre-treatment state. You are changed and life is different now. It's time to recognize and accept this and to go on. That said, it's not like flipping a light switch. Forgiveness is a process, and the intention is to free up what's stuck and causing the pain.

forgiveness is letting go of any hope for a better yesterday

There are layers to forgiveness: for example forgiving your body for not being perfectly healthy to prevent this diagnosis or forgiving your entire self and knowing that you did not cause yourself to get cancer.

Why forgive?

According to research (Fred Luskin), *"the practice of forgiveness has been shown to reduce anger, hurt depression and stress and leads to greater feelings of hope, peace, compassion and self-confidence. Practicing forgiveness leads to healthy relationships as well as physical health. It also influences our attitude, which opens the heart to kindness, beauty, and love."*

bitterness and stubbornness can also be signs that forgiveness is called for

We all know the obvious symptoms that could be relieved by forgiveness — feeling so angry, hurt or wounded that we want revenge or self destruction, constant brooding over a long list of grievances, feeling so guilty we don't know how make peace with ourselves or worry that the hurt could happen again. Bitterness and stubbornness can also be signs that forgiveness is called for.

In contrast to these limiting behaviors, which usually erect walls between ourselves and others, forgiveness is freeing. It means that we can move out of our previous position and move on with our lives. It enables us to feel reconciled with ourselves and with Spirit, God or Higher Power so that we can experience inner peace and freedom.

There are many forgiveness practices. What's important is to pick one that you think will work for you, and to use it as frequently and for as long a time as it takes for you to know that you are on the journey to forgiveness and have forgiven yourself. The process can be like peeling the layers of an onion as you go deeper with it and with yourself. And it can take much longer than you think it should, so be patient.

we can move out of our previous position and move on with our lives

Forgiveness is the best way to release negativity from within our core structure. When we are trying to find the place of inner balance, often times anxiety creeps in, but we don't know from where it manifested. This can be a tip-off we have not forgiven ourselves for what has happened in our life.

Practices for forgiveness

◌ Be clear on how you feel about what happened

◌ Be able to identify and speak out loud what specifically was not OK about the situation

◌ Share your feelings and what was not OK with one or two trusted friends, perhaps those who are presently on your healing team

◌ Decide that you will do whatever it takes to feel better

◌ Remember that forgiveness doesn't mean that what happened was OK. What you want is to find peace about what happened. You want to come to a place where you can honestly say, "it is what it is" and move on without a lingering emotional sting

◌ Recognize that the experience is in the past and whatever feelings or emotions you feel now as a result of that experience are from that past

◌ Remember that you cannot change what happened but you can change how you react to what happened

◌ Give up expecting things to be different

◌ Give up expecting events, people or things following your unspoken "rules" about how things should be or should have been

decide that you will do whatever it takes to feel better

◎ Put your energy into positive healing actions rather than reliving the past experience over and over again in your mind

◎ Remember that anyone or anything that has done something to you that needs forgiving has given you a gift – the opportunity for growth through forgiveness

More Practices

◎ Have a daily cue, reminder or vow, such as:

◇ Shaking hands is a cue to forgive myself

◇ When I clean my room, I am reminded of the cleansing and restorative power of forgiveness

◇ When I put my foot on the gas pedal of my car, I vow to accelerate the practice of forgiving myself

◎ Have a daily reminder that forgiveness is an embrace of yourself, across any judgments or negative thoughts, against all evidence to the contrary, and is more important than anything else

◎ Ho'oponopono forgiveness practice and prayer: I Love You, I'm Sorry, Please Forgive Me, Thank You: use as often as you wish

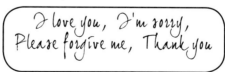
I love you, I'm sorry, Please forgive me, Thank you

◉ Affirmations on Self-Forgiveness and Release: Affirmations are statements you make with your conscious or analytical mind, that impress upon your subconscious mind. The subconscious mind reacts automatically with its storage of data to stimuli. For example, breathing is a subconscious action and we don't think about it, analyze it and create a system of doing it. We just breathe.

Here are a few, try to say these daily in order to forgive yourself for holding to any beliefs that do not serve you or for anything you feel has hindered your growth. Try these every day.

◉ Although there are things in life I cannot control, I completely forgive myself.

◉ I forgive myself for being hurtful or abusive to myself in any way.

◉ The love I have for myself is deep and pure.

◉ I forgive myself for being unkind to myself in any way.

◉ I am an amazing person who is very loveable.

◉ I am taking steps to be loveable.

◉ I love myself, I love myself, I love myself.

Meditation is also an important daily practice. Here is a meditation for forgiveness:

Give yourself half an hour without interruption. Turn off the computer, the phone; close the door to your room so you have privacy. If it feels helpful to you, you can light a candle, burn some incense or play some very soft and soothing background music.

Sit in a comfortable chair, with your body well supported by the chair so that you can relax fully. If you think you might get chilly, put a shawl or blanket around your shoulders. Sit upright with your spine erect and supported by the chair. This not only helps you to stay awake, it also is good for your spine to sit this way.

As you settle into the chair, begin to take some deep breaths, deep down into your belly, allowing your belly to expand with the breath. Slowly and gently exhale. I've repeated the one minute breathing practice from Chapter 1 for convenience:

      Begin by sitting comfortably, so that your body is fully supported by the chair you're sitting in. As you sink into being supported, gently allow your eyes to close. Take a long, slow breath in, to a count of 7. Feel the air filling your brain, traveling down your spine, then around to fill up your belly and your heart. Then suspend the breath – neither breathing in nor out – for a count of 7. Feel your brain relaxing; relax your neck and shoulders. Then a long slow exhalation, again to a count of 7, exhaling completely. This exhalation glides into another inhalation, to a count of 7...

◐ Repeat this 7-count breath 3 times. As you complete the third exhalation, let out a sound with the breath, if one wants to come out with the breath. ...

◐ Allow your breathing to return to normal, with more consciousness and spaciousness and depth.

Gently turn your thoughts and awareness to your body. Take a scan of your body and notice how it feels – where it's relaxed, where it's tight, any areas of pain or tension. If your attention is drawn to a place in or on your body, focus there. Continue taking deep breaths and with each inhalation, imagine that you are bringing Universal love to that place. With each exhalation, say, "I forgive you" to that part of your body. You can say these words silently or aloud, whichever you prefer. Continue with this for 5 or 6 breaths.

Then find another place that is painful or draws your attention to it, and focus there. Continue taking deep breaths and with each inhalation, imagine that you are bringing Universal love to that place. With each exhalation, say, "I forgive you" to that part of your body. You can say these words silently or aloud, whichever you prefer. Continue with this for 5 or 6 breaths.

Bring your attention and focus to your breasts, and where the cancer was detected and treated. Breathe deeply and imagine that you are bathing these parts of your body in love with each inhalation. With each gentle exhalation, say "I forgive you". Notice any feelings or thoughts that arise and continue to breathe in love and breathe out forgiveness. Continue with this for 5 or 6 breaths.

Next, tune into your heart. The physical heart is not only viewed as the center of the body and the source of lifeblood, but it is also the metaphoric center of love. As you focus on your heart, imagine that your heart has a voice. Ask your heart what it wants to speak to you. Then breathe, invite the heart to speak, and listen. Sometimes words come, sometimes thoughts come, sometimes feelings come. Listen and receive whatever comes from your heart. As you receive it, receive with kindness, compassion, love and forgiveness. Once the heart has "spoken", say "I forgive you" to your heart.

Sit and breathe and focus on your body and your heart for as long as it feels right to you. At first, it may only be a minute or two. As you continue with this practice, you will have different experiences and you may find that you are spending more time with it. However it happens, be gentle with yourself and know that you are doing this in just the right way for you.

When this part of the practice feels complete, say out loud:

" I love you (your name)"

" I forgive you (your name)"

" I forgive myself for my cancer and for any unkind thoughts or pain about my cancer"

" I forgive my body and I know that my body is healing in the perfect way for me"

" I forgive myself for being unkind to me in any way"

" I forgive myself for....any words that come to you to speak

Repeat these phrases 3 times, or more if you wish.

Let the words come to a close and continue with the deep breathing. Bring your awareness back to your body, sitting in the chair, feeling the support of the chair.

When you are ready, gently open your eyes.

If you have a journal, take a few minutes and write about your experience, feelings, and any insights.

This meditation is meant to be used as an ongoing practice over time. The more you do the practice, the deeper it will lead you and the more it will reveal about what and where to forgive yourself. Sometimes forgiveness takes longer than you think it should. Be patient with yourself, be kind to yourself, and trust this process.

Here is a link for an MP3 of this meditation: **http://www. sexyaftercancer.com/bookmp3s/**

APPRECIATION AND GRATITUDE

Whatever you focus on expands. Begin to cultivate what I call the attitude of gratitude. While it may seem simple, this is a powerful practice because when you are aware that you are going to speak about what you are grateful for, that is what you begin to notice. Look for what you are grateful for rather than what there is to complain about.

> *cultivate the attitude of gratitude*

Every time you sit down to a meal, begin by saying what you are grateful for.

Every night before you go to bed, tell yourself what you appreciate about you, out loud. At least 3 things, and not just the little things like the chores you did that day. Dig a little deeper, look into and from your heart, and notice the qualities about you that you appreciate. Speak those. Listen to what you say. Don't make this a throwaway time, but rather a time to connect more deeply with you.

> *when you look for what you can appreciate, you'll always find it*

Begin to tell others what you appreciate about them. When you look for what you can appreciate, you'll always find it. It feels wonderful to receive words of gratitude and appreciation and you'll feel great, too, as you speak the appreciation that you feel. The more gratitude I share, the more there is to speak. And whoever receives my words of gratitude and appreciation simply lights up.

You can keep a gratitude journal. Each day, write 5 (or more) things that you are grateful for. Then on those days when you need a boost, open your Gratitude Journal and read what you've written before.

A Day of Gratitude: Practices to Cultivate Gratitude

We all seek growth and expansion in our journey. We identify what we want, what drives us and set goals. But often there is a missing part that keeps us from having a feeling of euphoria and joy on our path. The feeling of bliss, goose bumps, and honest perfection.

I have found that Gratitude is the number one way to counterbalance any negative situation including episodes with negative people, worry over bills, fear or grief about breast cancer, anything that doesn't make you feel in alignment with Source, God, Higher Self (however you call it).

Morning Gratitude

Step One - Relax in a comfortable place.

Step Two - Begin to state the things you are grateful for in such a way that you are just saying anything that comes to your mind. Set a timer and for two minutes just do this without thinking too much about it.

Step Three - Choose one you are "most" thankful for. For example, "I am grateful for a loving partner". Then allow yourself to feel the warmth of the love that you feel for your partner. See his/her face, imagine you are looking into their eyes, or you two are laughing at a movie. Let the feeling consume you until you feel the joy all in your body.

Step Four - Hold this energy throughout the day and allow it to resonate with you.

◎   **Gratitude before meals**

As you sit at the table, take hands with the others who are sharing the meal. One by one, each person speaks about what they are grateful for and finishes with something that they are grateful for about themselves. If you're alone, say it to yourself.

◎   **Gratitude all around you**

Look for what's right in your world rather than what's not. As you develop the practice of looking for this, you will begin to see more and more of it.

◎   **Bedtime Gratitude**

Each night before bed, tell yourself out loud 3 things that
you're grateful for about the day. You can write them down in your Gratitude Journal and begin to collect your gratitude. In those inevitable times when you forget, you can look in your Gratitude Journal to inspire yourself and shift your thinking.

look for what's right in your world rather than what's not

An Appreciation Practice

You can do this with your partner if you have one, or invite a friend to share this practice with. It's simple and very powerful.

Every day, choose a time when you will sit down with your appreciation partner, either in person or on the phone. One of you begins by asking the other if they are willing to receive appreciations from you. Assuming they say yes, take a deep breath and imagine that you are looking at them from your heart.

expand your heart to receive and contain the appreciation – this is who you really are

Reflect on all the ways they have touched your heart, extended a kindness, or radiate qualities that you love and admire. One by one, speak each of these as you are inspired to give them voice. And do give voice to them so that your partner hears them and knows how you feel and think about them. Go deeper than something they may have done for you, and look into what you really appreciate, but might not typically say. Continue on until you have spoken all the appreciation, love and gratitude that is moving in you. Finish with letting them know that these are some of the things you appreciate about them.

Then switch. You partner begins by asking if you are willing to receive appreciations. Continue as above.

It is your job when you are the person receiving the appreciations to fully receive the words and the tone and feeling that is being expressed. Don't respond, don't debate, don't deny what's being said. Instead, believe that it's all true - because it IS true. It's the truth of your partner's experience. Just breathe, receive, and allow yourself to be moved by the words and how your partner sees you. Expand your heart to receive and contain the appreciation, and let it inform your core that this is who you really are. When your partner completes with their appreciations, say "Thank you." Nothing more. Nothing less.

My suggestion is that you do this practice daily. The more you do it, the more you will look forward to it, and the more you will begin to look and listen through the filters of appreciation. This is an exquisite gift to give and to receive. Be generous with it – you can easily do it with more than one person if you want!

ON CANCER AND COMMUNICATING WITH YOUR PARTNER

Contrary to what you believe or may have been taught, our partners cannot read our minds, nor would it necessarily be a good thing. The belief "If he/she really loved me, he/she'd know what I want..." is a zero sum game. It sets up unrealistic expectations all around.

The truth is that our partners want to please us. Our job is to tell them how to do that, and then let them do it, if they're willing. It's really quite simple, but not always easy given our beliefs or training. They want to please us in many ways and the best thing we can do to help them with that is to communicate with them and ask them to communicate with us.

So many issues can arise so quickly with a cancer diagnosis and treatment, and sometimes we hold it all inside, not knowing how to talk about it or afraid to talk.

What do partners of breast cancer patients care most about? In spite of what you may imagine or fear, studies show that the answer is simply this: Their loved one is alive and feeling well. The loss or alteration of a breast is almost meaningless in contrast. "I don't care what they take from you as long as I can see your face," is a common sentiment.

Most caring partners (both men and women) see their lovers as having many parts to love, and as being more than the sum of those parts. Nobody is promising there won't be ups and downs. The journey changes dramatically, and we can learn to navigate this new terrain with grace, kindness and curiosity.

While you're worrying about feeling less attractive, your partner may also be dealing with worry, anxiety, and maybe even guilt, wondering:

6 "Could I have been responsible?"

6 "Could I in some way have contributed to the cancer?"

6 "Will I become radioactive if I touch her, if I touch her breast? "

6 "Is her cancer contagious?"

And (perhaps feeling guilty),

6 "When will I be able to worry about myself for a change?"

we can learn to navigate this new terrain with grace, kindness and curiosity

It may be hard for you to figure out your needs and concerns, let alone tell them to your partner. You don't want to make light of what your partner has already done for you, so phrase your requests as carefully and positively as possible: "You've been working so hard, doing so much—and it's made a huge difference. What I really need right now is to be close to you and tell you what's making me nervous and anxious. I need you to listen, and maybe just hold me."

Communication—talking to each other, listening to each other—is the basis of any intimate relationship. But most people haven't a clue about how to talk about something as big as cancer.

Here are some tips to get you started

⚬ Find some time. Most couples have limited time together anyway. A breast cancer diagnosis adds more distractions. Even when you do get to talk, there are so many interruptions the conversation may go nowhere. Schedule some time in a quiet place where you know you won't be interrupted. Schedule it on a regular basis because there's a lot to talk about.

⚬ Start somewhere. Begin by talking about something comfortable and manageable—your vacation plans, even the weather. Once you're talking and feel connected, then you can work the conversation around to your fears, concerns, how the illness has changed you, and the importance of your relationship.

⚬ Talk, talk, talk. Even if your partner isn't a good talker, that doesn't mean he or she isn't listening. You may need to do most of the talking yourself but, believe it or not, what you're saying WILL be heard and it WILL sink in. Stop along the way to get feedback. Eye contact and touch can give your words greater meaning and emphasis.

○ Active listening, which is reflecting back the facts AND feelings, is a very helpful tool to let your partner know you hear them. We all want to feel heard and understood and active listening is a way to put yourself in their shoes, at least for a few minutes. The attitude of being curious about their experience helps immensely with this, as well as knowing that they are talking about their experience, not judging you.

we all want to feel heard and understood

○ Reassure your partner. Your partner may feel that you've got enough to deal with without listening to someone else's fears and concerns. Make it clear that you WANT to hear how he or she is feeling, that you're both in this together.

○ Bring in a third party. If you're both having trouble communicating, a visit with a therapist or coach can get the ball rolling.

○ Write it down. Sometimes it's much easier to write how you're feeling in the form of a letter or even a journal entry than to say it face to face.

the number one way to love your partner is to find out what they want, and then give it to them if you can

Breast cancer can be very stressful for your relationships, but good relationships can be made stronger by sharing the experience. Your partner may have doubts, and miss and mourn the "old" you, just as you may be doing. But that doesn't mean he or she is prepared to trade you in. "My husband stood by while I cried and screamed, and he hugged me when I let him get close enough," said Joan. "Our marriage is better now than it ever was before."

You can also communicate about your emotional, mental, spiritual and sexual fears, issues, desires, wants and needs. This can arise anywhere in the conversation process, so honor it when it does, whether it's from you or your partner.

Something I teach in relationship classes is that the number one way to love your partner is to find out what they want, and then give it to them if you can. Often we love the way we want to be loved instead of how our partner wants and needs to be loved. Understanding what they want and providing it can be transformational in your relationship.

Should you be in this relationship?

If you see yourself as damaged goods, you probably assume your partner feels as you do. But that simply isn't a given.

One consequence of feeling less than lovable is fear of being abandoned. It's true that in some cases a man or woman sees his or her partner's altered body as a personal reflection of his or her value—and just wants out. Other partners simply come apart under stress.

Curiously, divorce rates remain the same between couples who have experienced a cancer diagnosis and those who have not. Sometimes the shock of a cancer diagnosis pushes partners in a troubled relationship to consider the source of their problem and seek counseling, and therefore actually saves the marriage.

Overall, though, following a diagnosis of breast cancer, as many women leave their partners as are left by partners. They don't want to waste their time in an unfulfilling, unhappy relationship or marriage.

Of course, everyone is an individual. You may find YOURSELF responding unpredictably. One very independent woman became overwhelmed, uncertain, and very dependent when her breast cancer was diagnosed. This new "frailty" devastated her, and her marriage went through a rough spell till she finally returned to something of her old self.

Talking, telling, supporting each other

It would be nice to have a partner who understands and helps you feel better as you work to rebuild your confidence, but that may be unrealistic. He or she is probably suffering, too, and may be less able to express that suffering than you are. So each of you have all this emotion buried somewhere inside.

each of you have all this emotion buried somewhere inside

Breast cancer has become so common that most people have someone close in their life who has experienced the disease. There's no way to predict how anyone will respond, but there is no doubt that many partners are supportive and prepared to continue the relationship.

Women may find it easier to talk to one another, and lesbian partners may be particularly sensitive and supportive. It is also true, however, that a woman may feel especially vulnerable and personally threatened if her partner has breast cancer, knowing this disease is one that can affect her as well.

Talking about all your fears may be too overwhelming for your partner. If so, find a support group or start one. Or find a therapist or coach to work with you privately if that appeals to you more than a group.

FEELING SEXY? WHAT'S THAT???

Do you feel sexy?

Did you feel sexy before your diagnosis?

If so, do you remember what that felt like?

If not, what do you think it would feel like?

You might feel a bit self-conscious about this conversation. Feeling sexy and desirable as a woman can be shattered with a breast cancer diagnosis. Suddenly, we don't even feel feminine and it can seem like an impossible dream to feel sexy again.

"Sexy" has many connotations and most of us don't have a good idea of what it is. Let's explore this and see if we can tease out some of the elements of it. First we'll look at what is sexy to you about other people, then some of the qualities that make them sexy to you, and finally, how you can nourish and grow your personal sexiness. (Some of the ideas here are from my friends at Carnal Nation, which is an adult news website.)

> Suddenly, we don't even feel feminine and it can seem like an impossible dream to feel sexy again

Have you ever had the experience of being in the presence of someone who exuded sexuality, not by imposing it on you, trying to get attention or doing anything, but by simply radiating it? There's nothing predatory or invasive about it, it's just expressing through them.

When we meet that person who embodies sexiness, we know it immediately and feel it in our bones. But if pressed as to why they're sexy, we stumble and resort to clichés and stunted descriptions. Yes, there may be a visual component to it, but it's also more complex than that. Most people recognize that attractive physical traits can be easy on the eyes, but the person may not be captivating.

Conversely you've probably known individuals who are far from Hollywood beauty standards, but who make your heart skip a beat and stir your desires. It comes from someplace within, not in what is done or said. It's in how that person inhabits their body, how they engage with the world, how they think about themselves. It's that certain "je ne sais quoi."

It's subtle and noticeable but not over the top. There's no request or demand for attention, it's simply compelling and very inviting. Sexy people catch our eyes and attention. It's not about whether you want to have sex with them. They have the uncanny ability to broadcast this quality in entirely non-erotic situations, say while drinking a cup of coffee, gardening or just walking down the street.

What makes a person sexy?

What makes you sexy?

Did you ever know?

Are you sexy?

Are you already sexy and know it—or don't know it?

If you believe yourself to be sexy, how can you be certain?

Do you have the potential to be sexy?

My belief is that everyone has the potential, but not all of us realize it. Breast cancer is an opportunity to examine what this means to you personally, in a culture where sex is used to sell products ~ often with visuals of voluptuous breasts as a symbol for sex appeal. Consider: sexy may have nothing to do with breasts... we can free ourselves from the media stereotypes and create our own definition and experience of what is sexy.

Sexy is as mysterious as alchemy. And like alchemical magic, the ingredients are seemingly mundane, but can seem unfathomable to we mere mortals. Truly sexy people exude an energetic field beyond the knowable.

In the presence of sexy people, we viscerally experience that they possess something so desirable that many people want them, want to be with them, want to touch them, and perhaps want to be like them. Truly sexy people are completely at home in their own skin; know it and it's as natural as breathing to them.

Consider: sexy may have nothing to do with breasts... we can free ourselves from the media stereotypes and create our own definition and experience of what is sexy

What you believe to be sexy changes over time. For me, when I was in my 20's, it had to do with youth, strength, robust health, smoldering eyes, being comfortable in one's own skin, confidence and competence. There was nary a gray hair the on the heads of those who I thought were sexy; in fact, older people were not sexy at all to me.

As I have passed through several decades, what is sexy to me now is different: signs of a life well lived - things like wisdom in the eyes, not taking life too seriously, being comfortable in one's own skin, charm, confidence. Knowledge that their bodies and minds serve them well, a sense of openness and availability, the way they move and speak, the energy of self trust and being in personal integrity, not trying to impress me or anyone else are all qualities that are sexy to me. Some of the qualities have remained consistent over time and many have changed. Interestingly, as I've grown more confident and comfortable in myself, I find others with similar qualities to be sexy.

what you believe to be sexy changes over time

With the understanding that there may be no one grand secret to being sexy, let's explore some of the elements of sexiness, to understand what often feels like a mystery.

Confidence

Without exception, confidence is a necessary component. Many people who are sexy project confidence. It would be a challenge for a highly insecure person to come off as sexy. Think of what you see in their eyes and feel in their presence.

Confidence is about certainty in one's own abilities and place in the world. In a world of rapid change, uncertainly and doubt, another person's seeming sureness attracts us like a beacon of safety. We can fall into the habit of comparing ourselves with another's seeming security. When the boat of our life is pitched violently, the solid ground of another's life and safety of their embrace is as enticing as a calm port to a sailor in a storm.

The good news is that confidence can be cultivated.

But are all confident people sexy? No. I'm sure you've seen plenty of individuals who inspire sureness without stirring any sort of desire in you. There are many whose confidence I admire, even look up to, but they're just not sexy to me. Ruth Bader Ginsburg or Warren Buffet, for example, inspire great confidence in me, but sexy? Not in several lifetimes. Even so, confidence is an essential ingredient to the alchemical formula.

the good news is that confidence can be cultivated

Not many people effortlessly possess confidence—beginning in puberty we're plunged into the hormonal tides that can transform our childhood certainty about who we are into a lack of self-assurance or confidence. Think back to those days in your life and how important it was to fit in, to belong to the group, to know that you were somehow cool enough, smart enough, pretty enough, enough of whatever was important to you.

Many confident adults have struggled to find and nurture a belief in one's self. This is part of our process of maturation and individuation, how we come to know, understand and believe in ourselves. It's a heroic journey, and one we can undertake many times in our lives as things change and what once seemed solid and secure, shifts and moves.

We can look at others and see that they seem to have it all together. Yet we are only seeing them from the outside in. And we experience the world and ourselves from the inside out. The truth is that we're all in this process of self-definition and awareness.

When a breast cancer diagnosis is added to this mix, it's easy to feel like the rug has been pulled out from under our feet. We may feel betrayed by our body, drive ourselves crazy in an attempt to figure out how and why we got cancer, living in fear of the return of cancer, and not so sure of who we are. These are all possible reactions to having cancer. And this can completely shake our self-confidence to the point that we feel insecure in the most basic ways. Suddenly we can't count on things we could count on before, like our health or how our body functions. Coming face to face with our mortality has a big impact on our confidence.

coming face to face with our mortality has a big impact on our confidence

Cancer is a scary disease and it can be isolating. It calls into question what's important in life and what's not, what really matters. Our self-esteem and self-image are up for examination. Suddenly, rather than thinking we know who we are, we are that person with cancer, whether it's in the present or past tense. All the terminology about being a victim and a survivor can add to the insecurity we feel.

Strange as it may seem, this is a very powerful opportunity to look at what's important about who we are and what's not so important. It's a time when we can literally create new beliefs about life, now that life as we've known it has been threatened. Suddenly, we know that life isn't a dress rehearsal. It may be the first time you have faced your own mortality. Given that, how do you choose to live your life?

This window of opportunity to make conscious choices about who we are and how we want to live, can certainly feel intimidating. For those who choose to engage

life isn't a dress rehearsal

with themselves in this way and at this level, it can be an empowering experience that literally changes your life for the better. To know that it's possible to make these choices, and to make them, is beyond compare.

You may be familiar with this poem:

> *Dance like nobody's watching;*
> *Love like you've never been hurt.*
> *Sing like nobody's listening*
> *Live like it's heaven on earth.*

~ Mark Twain

Since no one gets out of life alive, why not create the life you've always wanted to live? Why not decide that you are confident? That you can be, and are, sexy and desirable? Who's going to say you're not? If you believe it about yourself, that's what you will transmit to the world, and you'll be experienced that way. I know, this sounds hokey. But this is the way it works. Really.

> *If you want to be truly sexy, the question is not "Do I look fat in this?" The question is "Do I feel great in this?"*

It's very helpful to view all of this from a positive vantage point, rather than self doubt. Remember that the mind can always cause mischief and is looking for chinks in the armor, so that it can come in and wreak havoc with us, especially as we commit to growth and change. Give yourself the benefit of the doubt. Know that you are doing the best you can, and that you are an extraordinary being. Looking from this perspective sheds a new light on everything.

If you want to be truly sexy, the question is not "Do I look fat in this?" The question is "Do I feel great in this?" This belief in yourself must be rock solid, without comparison with anyone else. If the frame of reference is constantly about others, confidence is a slippery slope at best.

Take an inventory of what's rock-solid and consistent about you, and what you love about you

These may be seemingly small things. For example, I love my smile and how I can light up a room with it. That is a 100% certainty about me that I can fully stand behind. From there, if I continue the list, eventually I'll get to greater beliefs, such as the power of the body and soul to heal itself, to become whole. I believe in human's potential for great good. Then I can be confident and believe in my own potential to offer my gifts to the world. Hence this book!

Here's a way to begin this inventory

Take a pad of paper or a stack of index cards. Begin with at least 20. On each one, write one thing that you love about yourself or believe about you in a positive way. It could be things like "I love my generosity of spirit", "I love that I see the goodness in every person I encounter", "I love my sense of hope," and so on. Without editing the list, just keep going until you have written at least 20 things that you love about you. Once you have completed the list, review it and notice how you feel as you read each statement. Do you feel rock solid about it? If not, could you with a little more belief in you? Do you need to change the words to make it feel rock solid? If so, do it.

You can continue to add to this inventory. I keep mine in a "love jar" that I have decorated and it sits on my desk. Every day, I pull out one of the statements and make it a practice to "be" that for the day. Doing this practice not only increases my love for me and my confidence, but it makes me totally solid and consistent in these qualities. It's not wishful thinking; it's my belief system and my Truth.

After making this list, really own your own beliefs and truths.

These are some big beliefs that may be challenging to hold onto at times. Each time our beliefs are challenged and doubt rears its creepy little head, we get to wrestle with our truths and stand up for who we know ourselves to Truly be. If we don't, doubt grows, colonizes the heart and becomes the norm. It becomes like a virus and spreads quickly.

Do you like to be around people who can't get beyond their self-doubt? Initially you may want to help them shift it; however, if they can't shift this, you lose interest in being around them ~ unless you are in the same place. Misery does love company, right? Does this have any correlation to being sexy? Not really, it's just the opposite.

at some point you'll realize that the fear and doubt can hinder you as you recover

That's not to say that we'll never feel doubt. Doubt comes in many forms, all designed to trip you up. A cancer diagnosis is a time when this can happen. If you begin to doubt your attractiveness, femininity or desirability, it can be a downward spiral that's difficult to shift. While fear and doubt is understandable as you navigate the diagnosis and treatment maze, at some point you'll realize that the fear and doubt can hinder you as you recover.

Sometimes doubt and some self-examination can lead you to make changes in your thoughts, your outlook, even your worldview. This can be a doorway to growth and to becoming who we always hoped and dreamed we could be - maybe even more than that. When we're growing, we can experience growing pains as we shed old beliefs and take on new ones that are more consistent with who we want to be. These growing pains can make us think that it would be easier to stay with the old ways ~ the old "ignorance is bliss" myth. Instead, what's important and helpful is to keep our vision and focus on where we're going, who we're becoming, informed by where we've been, without looking back and without regret or apology.

there's no point in hanging on to the idea of going back to who we were before diagnosis

Once we have the experience of wrestling with ourselves to change and create new beliefs, we begin to build confidence in the process. After all, we're being changed by our cancer diagnosis, whether we choose it or not. There's no point in hanging on to the idea of going back to who we were before diagnosis. Likewise, clinging to old limiting beliefs only causes pain.

Giving yourself the potential and experience of really changing from the inside out, is what assists us in evolving as we live. This is also very attractive, and part of being sexy. Think of your experiences in being around people who are living their lives in this way. It's exciting, compelling, and we want that for ourselves, right? This is what nurtures our belief in ourselves, as we create and embody our beliefs and truths. Standing in the Truth of who you are and what you believe in is rare and captivating. This kind of integrity is what draws others to us, like a moth is drawn to a flame.

Live *your* truths and convictions, but don't impose them on others.

Your list of rock-solid values, things you love about you and beliefs, are yours and no one else's. Understand that everyone has their own beliefs and values. Convincing others to accept and believe in your truths doesn't make you more right, more confident or better. It just makes you pushy. Pushy isn't sexy. It feels like a manipulation of some sort, instead of openness about who we are.

standing in the Truth of who you are and what you believe in is rare and captivating

Being able to sit with your beliefs and be nourished by them without the need to proselytize gives you the dependability and attractiveness of a lighthouse in a storm. Lighthouses on firm foundations are also attractive on calm clear days. Be the lighthouse, not the storm or the flotsam tossed in the wave. People will be drawn to the beacon that you are. Authentic confidence is truly a foundation of the alchemy of sexy. You will be radiant with this.

As you've been reading and digesting this exploration, there may be other qualities and characteristics that are part of the alchemy of sexy to you. What are those qualities and how do you feel when you are in the presence of people with those qualities? What is it about them that feels sexy to you?

Now that you have a better idea of the ingredients of what sexy is to you, how do you go about cultivating yours?

Practices to cultivate Sexy

☺ Make a list of what is solid and consistent about you, and what you love about you.

☺ Determine what's important to you and what's not at this point in your life to reveal your truths and convictions.

☺ Decide to embody and live by your truths and convictions without ever having to speak about them to anyone else.

☺ Look into your eyes in the mirror and see the light in your eyes. If you don't see it or feel it immediately, do the mirror practices described in Chapter 7.

☺ Make your Love Jar: take a pad of paper or a stack of index cards. Begin with at least 20. On each one, write one thing that you love about yourself or believe about you in a positive way. It could be things like "I love my generosity of spirit", "I love that I see the goodness in every person I encounter", "I love my sense of hope," and so on. Without editing the list, just keep going until you have written at least 20 things that you love about you. Once you have completed the list, review it and notice how you feel as you read each statement. Do you feel rock solid about it? If not, could you with a little more belief in you? Do you need to change the words to make it feel rock solid? If so, do it.

Put the statements in a "love jar" that you decorate in whatever way you wish. Every day, pull out one of the statements and make it a practice to "be" that for the day.

☺ Begin to train your thoughts to align with the belief that you are sexy and desirable, on your terms. When you find yourself thinking negatively about yourself, consciously choose to think about what you love about you. Over time, as you strengthen this way of thinking, you may notice that people are drawn to you, want to be around you, feel seen and accepted by you.

Look into your eyes in the mirror and see the light in your eyes

☺ Remember that sexy has nothing to do with showing your breasts or coming on to others in an artificial way. It's all about your confidence - belief in your personal qualities and things you love about yourself, embodying your principles and beliefs without needing anyone else to conform to your beliefs, being in integrity with who you know yourself to be, and the twinkle in your eye and energy that radiates from you when you live this way.

12

WHAT THE HECK IS SEX, ANYWAY???
LET'S TALK ABOUT SEX

Now that we've done a lot of inner healing and growing work, we've built a foundation for going a little deeper. We're going to explore the subject of sexuality from a few perspectives. We'll look at the physical changes to your body; we'll explore what sex really is (far beyond genitals, insertion and fluids exchanged). I will share a series of suggested visualizations, practices and tools that can be used to enhance and expand your ideas and experience of intimacy and sexuality.

We all have loads of beliefs and baggage about sex and sexuality

In a book discussing sexuality I think it's important to lay some groundwork and ask, "what is sex?" These are my personal views, some historical views and some current common views about sex. I'm not asking you to agree with my ideas, nor am I interested in changing your beliefs. I ask that you read this with an open mind and heart and entertain the possibility that you may find some truths contained here. Ready? Take a deep breath and let's dive in...

We all have loads of beliefs and baggage about sex and sexuality, some of which came from our religious upbringing, some from the media, and some from our schools, even from the government. Remember the "Just Say No" campaign? This was an attempt to have us ignore the natural urges and desires of our physical bodies.

Before written history, women were worshiped as goddesses, and as the source of fertility and life. Many cultures were matrilineal and matriarchal. You may have heard of the vestal virgins, about ancient fertility rituals like Beltane, which included outdoor sexual activity in the fields as a way to bless the coming sowing of seeds, growing of plants and an abundant harvest.

The mystery of childbirth and new life were revered. Because women were the ones giving birth, they were treated with reverence. They held the mystery and power that came with the ability to create and bear new life.

There are still images in ancient caves and sacred places that are evidence of this. Many European cathedrals are built on top of what were once ancient sacred sites to honor women, the Virgin and the Black Madonna. The cathedral at Chartres in France, for example, has an ancient site in the crypt and a labyrinth that is a remnant of these ancient practices.

In Greek and Roman mythology, male and female gods were equally revered and powerful and the culture was one of partnership. Rianne Eisler writes about this time in a wonderful book, *The Chalice and the Blade*, if you are interested in knowing more about this.

sex and sexuality have become issues of shame, guilt and embarrassment

It all began to change about 5000 years ago, when the shift to the patriarchy occurred.

People often fear what they don't understand, and find ways to manage or control what they fear. When men rose to power in government and religion they created the belief that the powers and pleasures of the body, especially the female body, were dangerous. While the patriarchy brought great benefit and progress in many ways, there was a good deal of oppression and suppression of women and the partnership way of life shifted to something else.

> When there is such a strong cultural focus on physical beauty and having beautiful and perfect breasts, it's easy to understand why breast cancer and its treatments are so devastating on so many levels

The pendulum of power is beginning to swing back today; however, we still live in a world where women are often shamed (or abused) because of the beauty and functions of their bodies. Along with this, sex and sexuality have become issues of shame, guilt and embarrassment, at the same time that they are highly valued. It's very confusing these days. And we don't talk about it much, if at all. Women's magazines are filled with articles on how to be sexy, be a better lover and have the perfect body. They're mostly based on what's wrong with us rather than what's right. There's very little published about what really goes on with us, nor are there places where we can speak candidly and safely about what it is to be a woman, much less a woman on the breast cancer journey.

I believe that this is part of why breast cancer is so traumatic to a woman's sense of femininity, desirability and sexuality. When there is such a strong cultural focus on physical beauty and having beautiful and perfect breasts, it's easy to understand why breast cancer and its treatments are so devastating on so many levels.

This is the elephant in the room!

- It's not talked about in the doctor's office

- We have a lot of taboos against talking openly about sex and sexuality

- Doctors aren't trained to talk about it and may therefore be uncomfortable talking about it

- We don't know how or what to ask.

This can be a very slippery slope!

I had the great good fortune to find my way to the Love, Intimacy and Sexuality workshops many years ago. This is where I learned to make the distinctions between love and intimacy and sexuality and to discover much more about sexuality.

Here's the essence of what I learned and believe about sex and sexuality

◊ Our bodies are designed for not only procreation, but also for sex and pleasure – just look and this is obvious. The procreative urge or imperative is very strong in all of us and "runs" us at times. We can also derive great pleasure without procreating. This can stop abruptly with cancer treatments.

◊ Sex is so much more than two body parts rubbing together and creating a release of fluids.

◊ Our entire bodies contain many erogenous zones – think about how it feels to have your ear gently nibbled, the inside of your thighs stroked, your hair gently pulled...and more...

◊ There are other forms of intimacy that support sexual intimacy: emotional, mental, physical, spiritual and energetic intimacy.

◊ Our sexuality is a natural function and there is nothing to be ashamed or guilty about.

◊ Being able to talk about sexuality, ask questions and learn is enormously healing and empowering.

Part of why sexuality is confusing and not talked about is simply because we haven't learned the language or had the opportunity to do so. Sex is so much more than something we can do with our genitals.

Sex is a multi-layered process and experience that includes:

◎ Our physiology and how our body functions

◎ Our thoughts and beliefs about ourselves, intimacy and sex

◎ Our feelings about ourselves

◎ Our relationship with our self and with our partner

◎ What we create and how we communicate with our partner

Let's talk first about the mechanics.

Breast cancer is a traumatic insult to our bodies. If we stop being sexual during or after treatment, the results can be similar to what happens when we stop exercising: the body parts lose their flexibility and elasticity, and can atrophy. With our genitals, the same thing happens, and we need some rehabilitation to regain and grow our sexual function and pleasure.

> *Being able to talk about sexuality, ask questions and learn is enormously healing and empowering*

As more time passes, problems can be more profound. Then you may lose interest, and it may take more effort to come back to your sexuality. It can be a downward spiral that begins to feel hopeless.

Perhaps the most frustrating change in your sexual life is the loss of libido, of "those urges." You've lost your hair, your breast is altered or gone, you've put on or lost weight, you have no energy, you're tired, you're nauseated, and you hurt in new places. No wonder you're not feeling sexy.

Anatomically, we have erectile tissue all around the genitals. Our clitoris extends beyond the small round glans under the clitoral hood above where the labia meet all around the vulva, pelvic area, groin and lower belly. Imagine your vulva with an area that begins with the clitoris and extends up and around from there and meets again at the opening to the anus, in a beautiful heart shape which extends deep into your body.

> Perhaps the most frustrating change in your sexual life is the loss of libido

We have a clitoral system, which responds and engorges when we get turned on. This is partly why it takes women longer to get aroused - there's a lot of tissue and it takes time for it to receive the blood flow to engorge. Remember feeling really turned on and the engorgement and tension of it? It's a lovely feeling. While engorging, we lubricate and get juicy as our body prepares for insertion, intercourse or play with toys. As we get more aroused, our breasts can feel a lot of pleasure, our pupils dilate and our body temperature rises. We may or may not orgasm or ejaculate. Much of this response is driven by the estrogen and testosterone in our bodies. These hormones drive our libido and much of our sexual response.

With chemo and hormonal therapies, this all changes rapidly. These therapies are formulated to reduce estrogen production so that any hormone-sensitive cancer cells aren't stimulated to grow. When estrogen production stops so quickly, we experience sudden menopause. This causes big changes in our vaginal and clitoral tissue. It becomes friable, so thin and delicate that it tears very easily. It's not as elastic and we don't lubricate as much. This is why touch and insertion of anything – tongue, fingers, toys or a penis, or intercourse - is painful. Estrogen also stimulates libido, so that also declines. We stop feeling "hot" as our libido takes a nosedive.

Something else happens. All these changes can cause us to be afraid –of pain, loss, not being desirable. When we're afraid sex will hurt, we can't relax and enjoy it. We can begin to avoid it. It's a downward spiral and can feel like your sex life is over. We think it will hurt, which makes it hurt more because the fear keeps our tissue contracted, and it hurts so we don't want to even try, and soon we're asexual.

This is rarely talked about in medical appointments. Did anyone discuss this with you? Many doctors say that they'll answer questions from their patients, but patients often don't know to ask, because this side effect of treatment is like a dirty little secret. Research shows that 40-90% of women experience sexual difficulties and 20 years later, 50% still do. While these treatments save and prolong lives, we don't have to pay with intimacy and sexuality.

Beyond the mechanics and physiological implications of breast cancer treatments, there are other factors to consider, which have a big impact on the physiology. This is the multi-layering mentioned above.

In addition to the mechanics, the layering includes how we think and feel about ourselves, as a woman and as a woman with breast cancer.

Depression and libido

Depression is a common result of both the diagnosis and the treatment of breast cancer, and it directly affects your interest in sex. If you're depressed, sex may be the last thing you want to deal with. You may even develop a real aversion to sex. A sensitive partner will pick up on this, but then, when you've recovered, your partner may continue to show no interest in sex, and you may assume it's because you're no longer desirable.

If you are depressed and unable to turn the corner, get help. Consider therapists or group support or a physician if you think medication might help. You've undoubtedly heard of the success of new medications, but you'll have to be careful. Some therapies for depression may cause loss of libido, including Prozac (chemical name: fluoxetine) and Zoloft (chemical name: sertraline). Medications must be carefully administered and monitored by a qualified medical professional (usually a psychiatrist). Effective dose levels are important and not always appropriately prescribed, and for many medications it takes three weeks or more for you to feel the benefit.

Depression, however, is too debilitating a condition to ignore, so be sure to seek help. There are some things that time alone doesn't heal.

Remember, I am not a physician and am not offering medical advice here. You should always speak with your doctor regarding any medication you are taking or wish to take as part of your treatment.

if you're depressed, sex may be the last thing you want to deal with

If you are taking tamoxifen or other hormonal therapies, talk to your doctor about which antidepressants are safe for you to take. Some antidepressants -- including Paxil (chemical name: paroxetine), Wellbutrin (chemical name: bupropion), Prozac, Cymbalta (chemical name: duloxetine), and Zoloft -- interfere with the body's ability to convert tamoxifen into its active form, preventing you from getting the full benefit of tamoxifen.

there are some things that time alone doesn't heal

Hormones and libido

You may find that it has become harder to get aroused, and even harder to experience orgasm. "It takes so long to make it happen," said one woman. This dullness of response—if you can call it a response—is a consistent complaint. Be open with your doctor, so that he or she can suggest appropriate medical solutions.

Loss of desire and drive may be directly related to your lower estrogen, progesterone, or testosterone levels, brought on by your breast cancer treatment.

If you're having problems with sex, you might want to try downplaying the importance of penetration and orgasm, at least for a while.

For some women who've had minimal interest in or opportunity for sex before all this happened, loss of libido may not be much of a problem. But if it is for you, talk to your doctor about the possibility of a hormone evaluation. A woman's sex drive is dependent on the hormone testosterone (the primary hormone in men), produced in the ovaries

you may find that it has become harder to get aroused, and even harder to experience orgasm

and the adrenal glands. A little goes a long way, and an adjustment may help restore sexual interest.

If your testosterone level is within normal range, more testosterone probably won't help. In fact, too much testosterone can produce acne, irritability, and male characteristics such as facial hair or a deepened voice. In addition, it's not known if "testosterone replacement therapy" is safe for women with a personal history of breast cancer.

Pain, nausea, and libido

Painful intercourse can destroy your interest in sex faster than anything else. Vaginal ulcers that arise during certain chemotherapies are a major source of such pain. The ulcers may be particularly severe in women who have had bone marrow transplantation, but they do go away when treatment ends. Women with genital herpes may have an outbreak of the disease brought on by stress and a weakened immune system. Steroids and antibiotics can cause yeast infections in the mouth and vagina. Pain medications, narcotics in particular, can also reduce libido.

Menopause, whether natural or treatment-induced, can cause thinning and shortening of the vaginal walls. Vaginal dryness (lack of natural lubrication) is another menopausal side effect. These conditions can contribute to pain during sex.

Nausea, a side effect of chemotherapy, can kill your interest in anything, particularly sex. And some anti-nausea medications depress libido.

When treatment ends, many of the treatment-related problems will end over time, which can help with the mechanics of sex. But this is not always the case and there are the other layers of this multi-layered process.

your most important sex organ is your brain

All this said about depression and medical solutions, there's a lot more to libido and sexuality than the mechanics of how our body functions or doesn't, and there's a lot more to sex than intercourse. In my experience, the more I expanded the possibilities and my thinking, the more hopeful I felt and the more pleasure I've been able to experience.

What's a Girl to do???

Your most important sex organ is your brain. Ever notice how your thoughts can lead to wonderful or terrible feelings? We talked in Chapter 3 about how you should not believe everything you think and why controlling what you think is critical to your healing.

With respect to sexuality, we can easily talk ourselves out of or into feeling sexual and aroused. While part of sex is mechanical, it's also true that our bodies respond to our thoughts and beliefs. Our bodies don't distinguish between what's happening physically and our thoughts of what will happen physically.

Skeptical about this?

Here's a quick experiment to demonstrate

Close your eyes and take a breath. Think about a juicy slice of lemon. Imagine picking up the slice of lemon, putting it in your mouth and sucking on it, the juice dripping over your tongue...What happened? Your mouth watered and puckered, right? Did you really suck on a lemon? No, but just thinking about it caused a physiological response.

We can also use our minds to create pleasure in many ways. Using your mind to create erotic feelings is a wonderful way to stimulate your sexuality. Here's another experiment to demonstrate this:

Allow yourself to daydream ~ close your eyes, breathe deeply to relax your body, and as you relax, think of a time when you were kissing that got you excited.

Who were you with?

Where were you?

What were you wearing?

Were you outdoors or inside?

Was it warm or cool weather?

Daytime or nighttime?

What happened?

Re-create the experience, and especially the emotional, physical and sexual sensations. Let yourself go fully into to experience....for as long as you like, savor the sensations.

I have recorded a guided visualization to assist you with this process. You can download it and listen so that you can relax fully into the process without having to think about it. Go to **http://www.sexyaftercancer.com/bookmp3s/**

What did you just experience?

Was it pleasurable?

Did you have a physiological response?

This is a powerful key to rehabilitating and expanding our sexuality during and after treatment.

Know that there are many areas on your body other than your breasts and genitals that can experience great pleasure.

Remember the first time you had a heavy kissing session, really made out?

How did that feel?

Was that making love?

Remember sitting in a movie theater holding hands, and that was making love?

What is it when two people sit and gaze into each other's eyes for an extended period of time? As you gaze and are seen, you begin to open. The first impulse may be to channel this intimacy into intercourse as your sex opens (or you feel a stirring in your genitals). If you continue to sit and breathe and gaze, you may find that your heart opens, your mind opens, your spirit opens and soars. Isn't this what we want from our most intimate experiences? To be fully seen and met, and to feel deeply connected to another?

> What is it when two people sit and gaze into each other's eyes for an extended period of time?

Intimacy has many more meanings than sex, genital sex.

In addition to sexual intimacy, there is

- emotional intimacy

- physical intimacy

- spiritual intimacy

- mental intimacy

- energetic intimacy

My wonderful teacher, Stan Dale, often said that "SEX" is an acronym for Sacred Energy Exchange and Spiritual Energy Exchange as well as Sexual Energy Exchange. If we expand our definition, then many things can come under the umbrella of sex.

> "SEX" is an acronym for Sacred Energy Exchange and Spiritual Energy Exchange as well as Sexual Energy Exchange

Doing yoga, breathing deeply, turning the attention inward and really feeling the body as it moves into a pose and holds it, is a deep spiritual intimacy with the self, a Spiritual Energy Exchange.

When I dance with my partner, we hold each other close, and look into each other's eyes. I feel the touch of our skin and bodies, the kiss of his breath on my cheek or neck. It is simultaneously intimate, romantic and sexual.

With this expanded idea of what sex is, I have sex every day in many ways!

> with this expanded idea of what sex is, I have sex every day in many ways

13

SEXERCISE!

During and after breast cancer treatments, many women experience menopausal symptoms including changes to genital and vaginal tissues, muscle strength and general sensitivity in the urogenital areas. These side effects are rarely discussed in the doctor's office and often come as a big surprise – yet another issue to deal with in addition to the other aspects of treatment. The good news is that strength, flexibility and tissue elasticity can be rehabilitated. It's possible, and can be fun, to rehabilitate these areas of our body.

breast cancer treatments can wreak havoc on our entire pelvic area

It's similar to undertaking a new physical fitness program – we start where we are and progress from there. I like to call this sexercise because it not only helps with pelvic function, but also helps ease the way back into genital sexuality, and it's a fun word! Just as muscles lose their strength and elasticity without regular use, breast cancer treatments can wreak havoc on our entire pelvic area.

While I've talked about expanding the definition of what sex is and explored ways to enhance intimacy and pleasure, many women and their partners are also interested in sex that involves the genitals and insertion, whether it's toys or invited guests that get inserted.

This is a subject that is challenging for some to explore because of the fear of pain or inability to have genital sex. So I'll begin with talking about the benefits of exercise and pelvic floor health, explain some of the anatomy that can be strengthened, and then describe ways to determine your current pelvic floor strength and ways to improve it.

regular exercise also increases blood flow to the genitals

Note: I am not a medical professional. Please consult with your doctor or health care provider before you begin this or any exercise program, and be sensible about what works for your body. Remember that baby steps are enough, and that "easy does it." I don't believe in the adage "no pain, no gain". Instead, I prefer "no pain, no pain." It feels much better and you will get great results.

A powerful way to whet sexual appetite and increase sexual activity is through physical exercise. Viewed as physical medicine, aerobic or strength-building exercise revs up hormones, flushes stress, whittles away fat and rejuvenates the body, filling us with renewed vitality, greater confidence and the glow of good health. Regular exercise also increases blood flow to the genitals, priming us for sex.

There is research to support this statement, and it shows how quickly things can change for the better.

Researchers at Bentley College in Massachusetts found that women in their 40s engaged in more frequent sex (about seven times per month) and found it more enjoyable than a sedentary group the same age. Since sex can be an act of endurance, improving cardiovascular fitness with aerobic activity such as walking, running, cycling or swimming for at least 30 minutes, three times per week, will help both partners perform longer and more often.

Similarly, A University of California study of middle-aged, sedentary men found that after just one hour of exercise three times a week, the men demonstrated improved sexual function, more frequent sex and orgasms and greater satisfaction.

Push-ups and sit-ups or crunches are also beneficial exercises to add to an aerobic routine. They strengthen the shoulders, chest and abdominals, all of which are utilized during sexual intercourse. Keeping these muscles strong helps increase strength and stamina, adding to prolonged, more pleasurable sex.

Unlike the muscles in our arms or legs, sex muscles are rarely active during the course of the day. However, by strengthening these "secret" muscles, we can enjoy sex play more, whether it's solo sex or with a partner. Kegel exercises firm the muscles of the vagina, helping women gain muscle control (to grip the penis or a toy) and reach orgasm more easily.

Pelvic Floor Health

The pelvic floor makes up a significant piece of our body's core, the essence of our very being. The foundation for all movement, balance, stability and flexibility begins in the pelvis. And in times of change, such as during cancer treatments, perimenopause and menopause, we can support our bodies — literally and figuratively — by creating strength in our cores.

Seven out of ten women have disorders of the pelvic floor. That percentage is even higher with women who have undergone chemotherapy or hormonal treatments for their breast cancer. It's not surprising, given that the pelvic floor supports the bones in the spine; structures the abdominal cavity — muscles and organs included; controls the passage of urine and stool; facilitates the childbirth process; and contributes to a woman's sexual pleasure and ability to reach orgasm. The good news is that many disorders of the pelvic floor are avoidable and correctable

It's helpful to visualize our pelvic floor as a hammock that supports all our lower organs. The flexibility and strength of this hammock come from a set of muscles and ligaments interwoven into the bowl-like pelvic walls, closing in at the base to form the pelvic and urogenital diaphragms. Entirely encasing the pelvic floor is a thin wall of fascia, or connective tissue, that covers, connects, and further supports the muscles and organs of the pelvic region.

Here is a simplified drawing of the pelvic floor. This part of our bodies is amazingly complex, and most anatomy texts devote a dozen or more drawings to its explication — it's miraculous how all the elements work together to serve their multiple functions. It's also true that the pelvic floor varies from woman to woman, so no two are exactly alike!

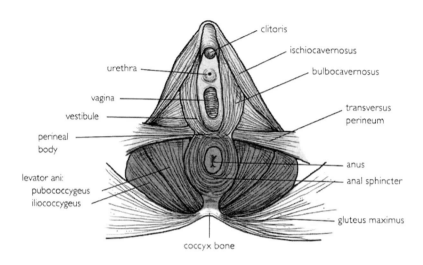

clitoris

ischiocavernosus

urethra

bulbocavernosus

vagina

vestibule

transversus perineum

perineal body

anus

levator ani: pubococcygeus iliococcygeus

anal sphincter

gluteus maximus

coccyx bone

*used with permission of Amy Stein, MPT

Situated at the base of the pelvic floor are the pelvic and urogenital diaphragms. Both are crucial for maintaining continence and aiding in sexual pleasure. The muscles of the pelvic diaphragm include the levator ani (a.k.a. "anus lifters"), which supports the coccyx, or tailbone. The pubococcygeus, one of the levator ani, is considered by some to be the most important muscle in the pelvic floor because it surrounds three essential openings: the bladder, vagina and rectum openings. And when the levator ani are compromised, so are these structures.

Chemotherapy and hormonal therapies can cause the pelvic floor to become weakened or more fragile, and the hammock can no longer provide support for its contents. The pelvic floor can be compromised whenever its muscles, tendons, ligaments, or nerves are weakened. This can happen as a result of large uterine fibroids, smoking and the associated chronic coughing, frequent straining during bowel movements, obesity, diets high in processed foods, menopause, hysterectomy, and cancer treatments. Even simple inactivity can lead to decreased tone, strength and flexibility of the pelvic floor.

When weakened, the pelvic muscles can't properly support a woman's organs; therefore women may experience some of the following symptoms:

- Urinary or stool incontinence

- Constipation or incomplete bowel or bladder emptying

- Diminished sexual satisfaction

- Painful intercourse

- Inability to reach orgasm

- Sagging or prolapse of the uterus, bladder, or rectum

- Low back or lower abdominal pain

If we build or rebuild these muscles throughout our lives, we are more likely to avoid weakness, tearing and prolapsing, surgery and stitches. In addition to practicing Kegels, there are numerous other exercises that can help strengthen and gently stretch the pelvic floor. These techniques have benefits to women of all ages.

Two options to help you rebuild these muscles are perineal massage and squatting.

Perineal massage is a technique that can help you connect with your pelvic floor muscles. Massaging the perineum increases circulation to the pelvic floor and makes it more supple and able to stretch. The perineum, as seen from the outside of the body, is composed of the skin between the vagina and the rectum. The perineal body extends inward from the perineum and serves as the insertion point of the eight total muscles comprising the pelvic floor.

perineal massage is a technique that can help you connect with your pelvic floor muscles

Whether you are doing this alone or with a partner, begin by giving yourself 30-60 minutes of private time for this so you don't feel rushed. You can do it on the floor, on the bed or on a massage table. Make sure your body is comfortably supported by whatever you use, and lie on your back with your back, neck and head propped up on pillows. You can also do this in front of a full-length mirror so that you can see what you're doing. Have some massage oil or cream or some lubricant handy and a box of tissues so that you can wipe your fingers (or tears, if you become emotional). You can also play some soft background music if you like.

The guidance below is given as if you are doing this solo. If you are doing it with a partner, you can modify as needed. With a partner, begin by looking into each other's eyes and agreeing that this will be a sacred exploration, that you'll go slowly and with love, and that whatever you discover will be a gift to you both.

After you've made your preparations, take some deep breaths as you lie back on the pillows, using your breath to help you relax. Gently close your eyes and imagine that this perineal massage will be pleasurable, relaxing and intimate, and that it will also help you to become more familiar with this part of your body, perhaps for the first time. Set your intention to love yourself, to be patient, go slow and to honor your body's wisdom.

Use your dominant hand (if you are right-handed, use your right hand), and put some massage oil or lubricant on your fingertips. Use enough so that your fingertips slide easily against each other, and rub your fingers together to warm up the oil or lube. Then begin with your index finger and thumb and gently begin to find the skin between the back of your vaginal opening and your anal opening. This is the perineum. For some women it feels good to be touched here; for others it's a bit numb because we sit on it most of the time or because we may have had a tear or cut to the perineum during childbirth. As you begin to touch the area, breathe deeply and just notice what it feels like to you. Take your time and focus your attention here, breathe and get to know this part of your body.

for some women it feels good to be touched here

Experiment with stroking, rubbing or more deeply massaging this area. You can use a motion that moves from the vagina to the anus and back to the vagina; make slow and long circles around the area; put more or less pressure into your touch to see what feels best. Using the index finger and thumb, you can gently squeeze the tissue from the sides, as if you were gently pinching the flesh. Using more lube or oil on all your fingertips, you can gently grasp the perineal tissue and squeeze it or knead it or pull it. There may be other movements that occur to you – try them.

The point here is to take your time, gently loosening up any tightness in the tissue here, moving it more as it warms up and becomes more flexible.

Some other things that you can try are:

◎ Hook the tip of your index finger into the vaginal opening and move it to the back of the opening. Gently pull as if you were stretching the opening to make it bigger.

◎ With your index finger inserted as above, gently apply pressure to the perineal tissue with your thumb and then move your thumb around.

◎ Using your index and middle fingers, stroke from the vaginal opening to the anal opening with your fingers parallel to each other and some perineal tissue between the parallel fingers.

◎ Stroking as above, gently massage the tissue between your fingers with your thumb

◎ Stroking as above, gently begin to move your fingers farther apart to stretch the perineal tissue

◎ You can also use both hands and use the same variations above, or use one hand near the vaginal opening and the other near the anal opening

As you move your fingers around, pay attention to what feels good and what is not so pleasurable. Remember to keep breathing deeply – breathing helps to relax the muscles and tissues, and holding the breath keeps them tense.

When the tissue feels well massaged, just place one of your hands, palm down, over the perineal area and rest it there for a few minutes. The warmth from your hand on the tissue is very soothing, and signals to your body that you are completing this activity. As you lie there, close your eyes, breathe deeply and notice how your perineum feels after this massage. If it's the first time you've done this, it may feel a bit tender. This is completely normal and is a result of the touch and stimulation.

As you continue with the massage over time, the tissue will become more supple and flexible.

When it's time to resume your day or evening, gently wash the perineal area with warm soapy water and wash your hands. Take a moment and look at your face in the mirror. You may find that you look more relaxed!

To download a recording of these instructions, go to **http://www.sexyaftercancer.com/bookmp3s/** Now you can listen as you try this out and not have to worry about juggling a book at the same time!

Squatting also encourages the stretching of the pelvic floor. No matter what your age, squatting is good for your pelvic floor, and the more you do it the greater ease and core strength you'll enjoy.

If you have problems with your knees, you can support yourself as you squat by using a doorknob. Open a door and stand facing the edge of the door where the knob is located. Stand with one foot on each side of the door, about 18-24 inches away from the door. Grasp the doorknobs and begin to gently bend your knees and lean back, as if you were going to sit on the floor. Lower yourself only as far as feels comfortable for your knees. The more you lean back and let the door hold your weight, the better this will feel. Take some deep breaths and relax into this gentle stretch.

If this feels comfortable and your knees are stronger, you can also squat without using the door. Begin by standing with your feet a little more than shoulder-width apart. Keeping your torso upright, bend your knees and lower yourself into a squat. You can use your hands to help with balance if you need that. Otherwise, rest your forearms on your thighs as you squat.

Whichever way you choose to squat, begin with 10-15 seconds in the squat position. Breathe deeply and relax as much as you can. Gradually begin to add time to the squat. Try adding 15-20 seconds every several days. Listen to your body's wisdom and do what feels good. As with any stretching, as you do more of it, your body will rapidly be able to do more. Don't push yourself beyond what feels relaxing and comfortable, and do keep making progress.

The pelvic floor is referred to by some as "the love muscles." This is because the pelvic floor muscles surround the vagina as well as the clitoris and contribute to a woman's sexual function and satisfaction.

Pelvic floor strength increases a woman's stimulation during intercourse due to increased blood flow, nerve sensitivity, and circulation to the area, which results in a heightened sensitivity to touch. Research says that women with strong vaginal muscles achieve better, longer, and multiple orgasms as well as increased ability to control the timing of them.

Yoga also offers many core-strength postures specific to the pelvic floor. By physically strengthening your pelvic floor, an essential piece of your core, you can increase your openness to significant transitions in your body, particularly those that result from cancer treatments.

Pelvic floor strengthening exercises

Many people have some problems isolating the pelvic floor muscles from the other muscles of the hips and pelvis. This is understandable, as the outer hip muscles are large and powerful. A key to success is to learn to recognize the feeling of just the pelvic floor muscles contracting, without contracting the buttock muscles. To remove the buttock muscles from the movement, you can practice pelvic floor contractions while standing with your legs wide apart and your heels out wider than your toes (a toed-in position of the feet). With your toes pointed in, you cannot contract your buttock muscles. Do not do this if it causes or increases your back pain, however.

Another image for helping to get the pelvic floor muscles in an exercise is to think of bringing the sit bones together and up. You can also think of drawing a fountain of energy up from the base of the pelvic bowl -- up through the middle of the body, and out the top of the head. This image helps connect the in and up action of the pelvic floor muscles with the other core muscles, and increases awareness of the mid-line of the body.

Stopping the flow of urine is a good technique for finding out how the pelvic floor muscles feel when they are in action. This is the first step in creating and maintaining a strengthening program for them. If you are able to stop the flow of urine completely and instantly, you are ready to embark on the exercise program. If not, the finger test described below will help you to recognize and assess your own pelvic floor contractions.

Insert two fingers into your vagina and contract your muscles. (If your vaginal tissue is very fragile, it will help to put a small amount of lubricant on your fingers, just enough to slide them inside the vagina easily.) When you find your inner squeeze, it will feel like the opposite of bearing down to make a bowel movement. It is a drawing in and up around your inserted fingers. You can aim to bring your tailbone and your pubic bone together, and while you may not notice this actually happening, using the image might get your pelvic floor muscles into a working contraction.

While you are doing this test, continue breathing -- holding your breath alters the way in which muscles are being used, and defeats the purpose of the test. The contraction you feel may be small, but once you locate a contraction you are ready to strengthen your pelvic floor muscles with exercise.

This step is an assessment of the strength and endurance capacity of the pelvic floor muscles:

First, test yourself for the length of time you can hold a pelvic floor contraction. To do this, repeat the finger test, but this time count the number of seconds you can hold the muscles up in the inward squeeze. This is a measure of muscular endurance, or how long can your pelvic floor muscles can go before they begin to tire. Make a note of the count you held the muscles in the up and inward squeeze.

After you know the length of time your pelvic floor muscles can endure, the next test is for the strength of the contraction. In other words, how many of these contractions can you perform before the muscle becomes fatigued? Perform as many of them as you can. Count as you go and make note of the number.

The third step is to clock how much rest you need between your contractions. Count as you did with the squeeze and make a note of the time.

The final step in the strength and endurance assessment is to test for the performance of fast working muscle fibers of the pelvic floor muscles. To do this, perform inward upward squeezes just as fast and as hard as you can, and count the number you can do until you can't do any more (this is muscle fatigue). Don't stop for a break until you are done with the whole set. Think of it as a set of repetitions like you would do in a fitness program.

Make note of all these measurements so that you can see how you progress with the strengthening program.

start right where you are

The goal for the pelvic floor strengthening program is to hold 10 slow squeezes for 10 seconds each, 3-6 times per day. Start right where you are. By writing down the numbers from your assessment, you can increase as you go along. It is a matter of challenging yourself to do more contractions and/or to increase the amount of time you hold them. Both activities will result in stronger pelvic floor muscles, so increase either or both, until you reach 10 squeezes held at 10 seconds 3-6 times each day.

Repeat the finger test every few days to help you monitor your progress. When the finger test shows you that your pelvic floor muscles are stronger, add one or more seconds and/or a few more reps to your program.

As with any exercise program, starting your pelvic floor-strengthening program too vigorously can be a potential source of injury, fatigue or frustration. Start from the strength level you possess now and build slowly but consistently. Keeping track of the number of reps and seconds held as you go will allow you to increment the level of challenge in a sane and results-oriented way over the long term.

While in the shower perform an inner squeeze for 6 seconds. Keep doing the squeezes the entire time you are in the shower.

Every time you finish emptying your bladder do 3 strong inner squeezes, holding for 5 seconds each. You can also do the squeezes while you are driving, as long as you don't get distracted.

Practice pelvic floor muscle contractions as you make love. This will enhance your sex life while it helps your back!

Other Stretches and Exercises

The following pelvic stretches will help keep the muscles used during sex limber and flexible and can help facilitate orgasm. Each stretch can be done in the bedroom on a firm mattress or on the floor. Wear either loose clothing or nothing at all, and consider playing your favorite music. As these exercises can arouse strong sexual desire, you might want to try these with your partner if you have a partner.

Pelvic Lifts

Lie on your back with knees bent and slightly apart. Feet should be flat on the floor and arms at your side. Inhale, tightening your abdominals and buttocks. Lift your pelvis until your back is straight and parallel to the floor. Take care not to arch your back. Breathe as you hold the position for at least 10 seconds. Exhale as you lower your body and repeat the exercise.

After you complete your lifts, try a few pelvic bounces, an exercise that can evoke powerful sexual feelings.

As with the pelvic lift, knees are bent and slightly apart. Your palms should face up. Inhale and lift your pelvis just slightly off the ground. Then, exhale and let it down so your lower back bounces gently against the floor. Experiment with variations. Your goal is to feel a sense of openness and release.

The Butterfly

Lie on your back with your knees bent. Your feet should be together and flat on the bed. Next, pull your feet in until they touch your buttocks or are as close as feels comfortable. Turn your ankles so the soles of your feet are facing each other and touching. Your knees will point out to the sides of the bed.

Lower your knees toward the bed, taking care not to force them down. You or your partner may gently press downward on your inner thighs. When your knees are as far apart as is comfortable, hold for 60 seconds. Gently bring the knees back together with your hands and relax.

This exercise can also be done sitting up, back-to-back with your partner. Sit up as straight as possible with your spines pressed gently together. Relax your shoulders and keep your head in line with your spine. Bring your feet in as close to your body as possible, and turn them so your soles touch and knees point out. Clasp your feet. Breathe deeply and watch as your knees begin to lower, taking care not to force the knees down.

if you don't love your vulva, who will?

The butterfly is also beneficial for menstrual irregularities and urinary problems.

The final exercise is to start loving your body. The better you feel about your genitals the more your sex life will improve. The research says that women who have positive genital self-image, who feel good about their genitals and comfortable with their genitals, are six times more likely to have sexual satisfaction than women who are not. If you don't love your vulva, who will?

When you have some private time, sit with a hand mirror and look at your vulva. Notice the colors, shapes and textures. Just look. And breathe. Each woman's vulva is as unique as her fingerprint. It looks like a beautiful flower. As you look as your vulva, begin to think how beautiful it is, how much pleasure it can bring you, how amazing it is in its capacity during birth and genital sex play. Say some words out loud to your vulva, things like: "You're beautiful." "You bring me so much pleasure." "I'm happy that you work so well!"

You can also draw a sketch of your vulva. Do this as a way of honoring and loving your vulva. You can use colored pencils or pastels or crayons if you have them. The colors of the vulva are beautiful.

each woman's vulva is as unique as her fingerprint

Some women like to name their genitals as a way of loving them. I've experimented with this over the years and at various times my genitals have gone by "Petunia" and "Miss Kitty." To me it feels playful and honoring and opens a door to talk about my genitals in a less clinical way.

No matter what you choose, make sure that it's what feels good to you and assists you in loving yourself more.

14

THE PLEASURE OF SELF-PLEASURE

As I've mentioned earlier in the book, you don't need a partner to feel sexy, be sexual or have sex. Part of this is knowing what brings you pleasure in your body. Since your body is changed, what brings you pleasure may have also changed. During and after treatment are excellent times to get to know your body as it changes.

I'm not only speaking of masturbation, but of discovering what other parts of your body enjoy being touched, stroked and kissed.

Give yourself an hour to be intimate with you. Put on some soft music, take off your clothes and lie on your bed. Begin to gently stroke your face, and slowly and gently, stroke yourself from head to toe. As you do, notice what areas like the touch, which don't feel it or are numb and those where it doesn't feel good. Experiment with oils and lotions, with light or firmer touch, with feathers or other things with different textures on your skin.

> *since your body is changed, what brings you pleasure may have also changed*

You will find a recording to lead you through this self pleasure discovery process and let yourself be gently guided here: **http://www.sexyaftercancer.com/bookmp3s/**

In chapter 15 you'll learn how to make a Pleasure Map.

While you're recovering from treatment, try concentrating on pleasure from touching, kissing, and imagery, rather than genital orgasm. De-emphasizing vaginal orgasm may actually allow it to happen again sooner than you expected.

go slow and don't have any expectations

When you are ready to experiment with genital sex, the best advice I can give you is to go slow and don't have any expectations. Sometimes we put pressure on ourselves by thinking we need to feel a certain way or achieve orgasm, and that pressure can derail our pleasure and cause frustration.

When we're feeling frustrated or judging ourselves, guess what happens? We stop relaxing, and that can make intercourse painful. Feeling pain can cause us to withdraw or think it's not going to happen. Sexuality goes out the window.

So relax. Go slow. There's no rush and nowhere to go. Not sure how to do that?

Here's a suggestion

A wonderful way to start is to get naked and lie in bed with your partner, looking into each other's eyes and breathing together. This allows you to establish a connection between your eyes, your hearts and your bodies. Then begin to gently stroke each other from head to toe, kissing if you like, all with no agenda other than being present with each other. If nothing else happens, this is a great way to build intimacy. If more happens and you feel moved to include your genitals, it's probably a good time to use some lubrication. Begin with fingers and massage. It's very helpful to "warm up" your vulva and vaginal areas before attempting penetration.

look into each other's eyes and breathe together

Think of it as kneading dough before it rises – it's important to work the dough to activate the yeast and make it more supple and elastic. It's similar with your genital tissue, especially if you're menopausal. Lubricating, warming up and gently stretching these tissues feels good, and it prepares you and your partner for further penetration. For the first time, this may be as much as you want to experience. Let your body and your heart guide you, rather than what you think should be happening.

There is a recording to guide you in this process. Go here **http://www.sexyaftercancer.com/bookmp3s/** to download it so you can experiment with it.

When you are ready for genital penetration, remember to go slow. Use plenty of lube, warm up and keep your body relaxed. Only when you feel really ready should penetration be attempted (including penetration with fingers or tongue). Use more lube than you think you'll need, especially if you're using condoms. Condoms absorb lube like a sponge absorbs water. Have plenty of lube nearby for more application.

think of it as kneading dough before it rises

If you're using condoms, use a water or silicon-based lube. Oil-based lubes degrade latex, which will destroy the condom's effectiveness. For an article on choosing a lubricant, please see my website **http://www.sexyaftercancer. com/articles**

What about Frequency?

Most people have wild ideas about what goes on in other people's bedrooms. Give yourself a break: The carefully researched book *Sex in America* (by Michael, Gagnon, Laumann, and Kolata) tells us that Americans have a lot less sex than the movies, television, and the guys in the locker room would have you believe. The averages reported in that book are:

- seven times a month between ages 30 and 40

- six times a month between ages 40 and 50

- five times a month between ages 50 and 60

For people over 60, the numbers continue to decline. But although you may assume that no one in their 70s and 80s has a sex life, that's just not so.

Molly, 78, described her sex life after breast cancer treatment: "I stopped the action for a while, and then we went back at my request. He was waiting for me to give him the go-ahead." Hilda, an 82-year-old breast cancer survivor, explained that she didn't have a lover "at the moment." Sex goes on even into the 90s for some.

Don't let the myths about other people's sex lives get in the way of what's happening in yours. And remember that there are exceptions to every pattern.

don't let the myths about other people's sex lives get in the way

Also remember that this is the classical definition of sex, which is genital sex. Using the expanded definition of Sacred Energy Exchange, you can be much more sexually active in more ways than these statistics and stories.

15

LET'S GO ON A PLEASURE HUNT – PLEASURE MAPPING

When we talked about sex and what it is, we opened up the possibility that it's much more than breasts and genitals being stimulated. Our entire bodies are zones of pleasure, sensuality and arousal if we open our minds to that possibility.

That idea, coupled with changes in our bodies as a result of treatments, is the perfect opportunity to create a Pleasure Map. What I mean by this is to learn where we feel pleasure in our bodies so that we can communicate this to our partners to increase pleasure for both.

My recommendation is that both partners create a Pleasure Map.

> *our entire bodies are zones of pleasure, sensuality and arousal*

Here's the process:

Set aside an hour or so when you and your partner can be undisturbed. Put on some soft background music and set up the space for the activity: make sure the room is warm enough for you both to be naked; have something soft to lie on if you're not in bed; have plenty of lube; make sure your fingernails are trimmed so you won't inadvertently scratch each other; have a glass of water in case you get thirsty; have some large pieces of paper and colored pencils, markers or crayons to draw the Pleasure Map. On one piece of paper, draw an outline of a head, face and neck.

Begin by looking into each other's eyes and take a few breaths to establish a deeper connection between your hearts and bodies. Spend a few minutes talking about what you want to do here: one of you will guide the other on an exploration of your body so that you can make a Pleasure Map. The purpose is not to get aroused and be sexual, but rather to explore your body to learn where it feels pleasure and what feels good. The one being explored is the one who guides the other about where and how to touch. The "explorer" agrees to be guided and to be curious. Agree that you will switch and make a Pleasure Map for the "explorer" at another time. It's best not to do this simultaneously; rather, focus on one at a time so there's no distraction or comparison.

Lie on your back and have your partner sit or kneel beside you as you prepare to make the Pleasure Map. To begin, guide them to gently stroke your face and head. As you are stroked, bring your attention right to where their fingers and hands are moving – notice how it feels.

Do you like the pressure?

Is it fast or slow enough?

Does it feel good?

Tell them what you like, especially any areas that feel good. As you do this, your partner can take a few moments and make marks and notes on the drawing of the face and head about what you are saying. For example, if you like the sensation of having your forehead stroked slowly and lightly from side to side, your partner can draw some light horizontal lines on the forehead and make a note beside it that says, "light stroking from side to side with fingertips."

Slowly and gently explore your entire face, head and neck, noting all the pleasure places. Take as much time as you need for this. Please don't rush! In addition to their hands and fingers, they can explore with their lips, cheeks, forearms and hair. Be creative and learn what brings you pleasure.

This may be enough for the initial mapping. When you feel complete with this initial map, whether you stop here or continue, take some time to look at the map and talk about what's there, making any additions or changes based on what you see on the map.

tell them what you like, especially any areas that feel good

In subsequent sessions, you can either take turns with various areas of your body so that you alternate making each other's Pleasure Maps, or you can complete with your entire body before switching to your partner's body. Talk about what feels right to the two of you.

Make maps for your entire body, head to toe and front to back. You may discover that you are creating a map book!

When you are at the pelvic and genital areas, have one session (or more) devoted to these areas. Make both external and internal maps. When making the internal map, use enough lube for ease of movement, but not so much that everything is too slippery. Really take your time with this internal map. Have your partner gently place one finger just inside the opening to your vagina and then move it slowly around using only the fingertip. Notice where it feels good, where it may be numb or have no feeling and where the touch doesn't feel good. Experiment with less and more pressure and with different finger movements: circular finger movements feel different than back and forth like a windshield wiper and different than moving the fingertip in and out. Try as many movements and pressures as you think of and note how each one feels. Then have them insert a finger farther inside all the way to the knuckle. Have them insert two fingers, or three fingers. What you'll probably discover is that there are many areas that have a lot of sensation, some that have no sensation and some that the sensation is painful or unpleasant. That's the purpose of the Pleasure Map, to discover the terrain of your body, inside and out.

> go slowly –
> remember that
> baby steps are fine
> to take

Once you've made your Pleasure Maps, you can use them in many ways. They are meant to be guides for your pleasure. You might choose to use one map one day and another the next day. You may discover parts of your body that are more pleasurable than you had imagined. You may find that the maps change over time. You may discover hidden treasures.

Have fun with this and know that this type of intimacy is rare and precious. You are opening doors to deeper intimacy than you may have previously experienced or imagined. Be gentle and tender with each other as you become Map Makers....

For a recording to guide you in making pleasure maps, go to **http://www.sexyaftercancer.com/bookmp3s/** to get the download. Have fun being a Map Maker!

Please don't feel daunted by what I'm suggesting above. I want to lay out the entire range of possibilities for you here. Use whatever part/s of the instructions appeal to you. Go slowly – remember that baby steps are fine to take. You might want to start with the face, head and neck and use what you discover there for a while, then continue with another area of the body. Or you might want to do more. Rather than see this as a big hurdle to achieve, let it be an inspiration for you to get to know your entire body.

16

SEX AND THE SINGLE WOMAN WITH BREAST CANCER

*G*etting your mojo back after breast cancer is challenging enough when you're in a relationship or married. What about when you're single and looking for a partner?

Breast cancer treatments can leave you feeling like you've just been through a war, that your past has become ancient history and you are now a victim/survivor. What happened to the woman you were or hoped to be? When treatment ends, many of the treatment-related symptoms begin to fade. You begin to think about more than just getting through the day. You know that you are going to live and you start to feel like a woman again. You begin to think about connecting and dating, intimacy and your libido and sex.

It's a whole new world for you and you get to learn how to navigate this new terrain with the new you. The dating world may feel a bit daunting. You may feel a bit tender as you contemplate it. If you've done any Internet dating, you may have had the experience of being chosen or not based on your photo. It can seem like the visual impact is the only one that matters.

you start to feel like a woman again

If you thought it was hard to find Mr. or Ms. Right before breast cancer, the ante has just been upped substantially because now you may have to explain a few things and get over a few personal hurdles. But don't let anything stop you from getting back into the dating scene and enjoying the intimacy that's such a worthwhile part of life.

How do you know when you're ready to get back into connecting and dating?

If you find yourself thinking about dating and how that would be, you are probably ready. That said, go at the pace that feels right to you. If you've done the exercises and processes in the other parts of this book, you now have a good sense of who you are, what's important to you and what's not, what you love about yourself, that you are sexy and desirable, and how to tune into your own wisdom. This is so much more than many people ever experience about themselves. That self knowledge is a big bonus for you as you begin to connect, date and explore with potential partners.

You may decide that you simply want partners for activities. You may want to date casually until you are ready for more. You may know that you really want to get into a romantic and intimate relationship. Or you may be somewhere else about this. Wherever you are, you are in the perfect place for you. Honor that and trust what you know.

if you are thinking about dating, you are probably ready

Let's start with one of the big questions:

When do you tell a date about your cancer experience? That is the $64,000 question!

This may feel like the elephant in the room to you because of what you've been through with your diagnosis and treatment. But remember that the person you are getting to know didn't know you then – they didn't know what you looked like, how you thought, how your body responded.

There may be no "perfect time," but you're not obligated to spill your entire medical history on the first date. Saying, "Did I mention that my breasts are made out of my belly?" before the appetizer is a good way to guarantee that they won't stick around for dessert. Take the time to let them get to know you first— and vice versa.

experiment a bit and do what feels best to you

In talking with many women, some choose to talk about it on the first date and others choose to wait until they feel a sense of possibility for intimacy with a person. There's no right or wrong way to do it. It's a very personal and individual choice. It may be best to experiment a bit and do what feels best to you. The timing of when you want to share this may also vary with how long it has been since you completed treatment – as time passes, and you regain some balance in life, you may not feel compelled to define yourself by these experiences.

One friend decided that she wanted to begin dating shortly after she completed chemotherapy. Her hair was growing back and she had a sassy short cut, and she was regaining her energy. She put a personal ad on the Internet and began it by saying that she had recently completed cancer treatment and was excited about life in ways that she hadn't been before. The ad went on from there. She received many responses to her ad and had several coffee dates in the following weeks.

On a personal note, I was single when I received my diagnosis. I met my second husband at the beginning of my treatment journey. It was during a casual weekend outing on a houseboat with mutual friends and we just started talking. As the day passed, we talked, cooked together and got acquainted. He was going through a divorce and I was just beginning my cancer journey. There were some sparks of attraction and the conversation in my head was, "We'll just be friends. He'd never be interested in me because I'm damaged goods now and no one will want to be with me." And so on.

> beauty is in the eye of the beholder, not in how we judge ourselves

Over dinner and wine, the conversation got more intimate. The sun set and later, I retired to my bed, sleeping under the stars on the roof of the houseboat. I drifted off to sleep. Some time later, I felt someone cuddle up to me and begin to stroke my face. We kissed and I started to cry. He asked why I was crying and I said because as soon as he saw my body, he'd see how damaged I was. He gently reminded me that he'd seen me in my bathing suit all afternoon, and he didn't know what I was talking about. He told me I was beautiful and that he was very attracted to me. That stunned me, because I was certain that I was "damaged goods." But beauty is in the eye of the beholder, not in how we judge ourselves or our perceived shortcomings.

Over time we became lovers and I knew I was falling in love. I went into the hospital for an additional surgery – a partial mastectomy and lymph node dissection. He visited me every day in the hospital and was with me when the surgeon came to report that the nodes were negative. He took me home from the hospital with a very large bandage and a drain. I knew inside that it was only a matter of time until he saw me and rejected me as damaged goods. I felt so deformed.

That didn't happen. He kept loving me and I did the inner work I needed to do to accept, forgive and love myself – many of the exercises and processes you've read so far in this book.

> there's no cookie-cutter approach - each situation is different

During my treatment, which was radiation, many mammograms and breast exams and blood tests, we continued to be sexual. The power of our love was a big part of my healing and recovery. We moved in together and 2 years post surgery, we married. Two years after that, despite the risks and the odds after cancer, I had a baby – my miracle baby. I share more about that later in the chapter on family planning and fertility.

Going farther forward, he and I had many marital difficulties and divorced several years later. This time I also had a young child. But over time I realized that the two things I had feared the most – having cancer and being a single parent – hadn't killed me. Just the opposite, they were opportunities for enormous growth and have been some of the biggest gifts of my life.

Single again, I had done the inner work to know that I was an attractive and desirable woman. I experimented a lot with when to tell my dates my history of cancer. What I discovered is that there's no cookie-cutter approach, and that each situation is different. As I relaxed within myself and had more and more time post treatment, it became less of an issue for me. And when it was no longer an issue for me, the elephant in the room diminished and became a part of my history.

Not every man I dated handled the information well. That conversation became a litmus test for me as to who got the opportunity to be with me and who didn't. Here are a few thoughts to help you determine if you have a potential keeper.

How to Tell the "Keepers" From the Ones You Should Throw Back in the Pond?

You know you've found a keeper (this one's worth exploring) if:

- They treat you like a woman.

- They're amazed by your strength.

- They find you beautiful and sexy, and love to kiss your scars.

- They mean it when they ask, "Are you okay?"

- Their priority in bed is satisfying you.

- They are in it for the long haul and treat their time with you like a gift.

Throw them back if:

- They treat you like a charity case who should consider herself lucky to have any partner in her life.

- They don't want to hear any details of your cancer or treatment.

- They stare at your chest like a detective, trying to figure out if your breasts are real.

- They are worried that "the rest of you" won't be in working order.

- It's all about them in bed. They assume that if they are happy, you should be too.

- They won't commit to a relationship; after all, you might get sick again, and they couldn't handle that.

When you do feel that the time is right and the partner is worthy, then you can tell them you had breast cancer—emphasis on "had." Your disease shouldn't be the elephant sitting at the table with you. It was a challenge that you took on, fought and won. Your partner should be honored to be dining with a magnificent warrior goddess. Some women are more outspoken than others and don't mind answering personal questions about their cancer and treatment. If you're not one of them, remember that it's okay to say, "If you don't mind, I'd rather not discuss that right now."

your partner should be honored to be dining with a magnificent warrior goddess

'Caroline', from the United Kingdom, got lucky with her new partner, who had been a friend of hers right before her diagnosis. "He saw me when I was bald and in bad shape from chemo. He also knew I'd had surgery, but I didn't need to spell out to him that I'd had a mastectomy—and I was able to be naked when we had sex. However, I'm well aware that this may not be the same in future relationships."

Be prepared for the possibility that your date may not be mature enough to deal with this information. A good thing to remember if this happens is, this is about them, not you. They are revealing their own fears and that is not a reflection of who you are.

Going Shopping

Once you've found a partner, if all goes well, you will wind up at the point of intimacy. Do not panic. Go shopping.

If you've had a mastectomy and haven't had reconstruction, ask your breast surgeon, a friend who's been there or the American Cancer Society, to recommend a good mastectomy boutique. Many of the nicer department stores can also help in their lingerie department. Ask if they have someone on staff who works with breast cancer patients and mastectomies. Wherever you go, you'll be fitted for a prosthesis or a breast form. This will be fitted to match your other breast. Then you can either buy a special bra or have pockets sewn into a regular bra. You can even buy press-on nipples if you have had reconstruction but haven't had your nipples done yet. When you shop, bring along a blouse or dress with you so that you can check the look and fit.

First, buy yourself some beautiful lingerie, as sexy as you like. Look at bras, camisoles, sleepwear, panties, even slippers. Take your time and try things on, and see what appeals to you and makes you like the way you look. The lingerie can be as revealing or modest as you like. Unless you enjoy the style of Frederick's of Hollywood, you may not find what you like there. You can shop at stores where you have in the past or you may already have some wonderful lingerie. Try that on as well to see what you like.

buy yourself some beautiful lingerie, as sexy as you like

Next on the list: lubrication, especially if you're postmenopausal or if meds like tamoxifen or aromatase inhibitors are blocking your estrogen production. Estrogen deprivation can make the vaginal tissues thin and dry, which can lead to itching and irritation around the vagina and urethra. In extreme cases just walking in snug pants can tear the fragile skin.

Go to my website **http://www.sexyaftercancer.com/ articles** for an article on how to select a personal lubricant.

There are many over-the-counter personal moisturizers; some are for daily use and others give you extra comfort during sex. Note that moisturizers and lubricants are different products. Moisturizers are formulated to help the vaginal tissues retain moisture to help with flexibility. They're good to use all the time, whether you're having genital sex or not. Lubricants are formulated to reduce friction between tissue during genital stimulation and insertion. There are also moiturizing lubricants.

moisturizers and lubricants are different products

Dryness will be less of a problem if you stay genitally sexually active. With proper stimulation where the blood supply to the vagina is increased, not only does lubrication improve, but so does the elasticity of the tissues.

Last on your list: protection. Of course, breast cancer doesn't make you immune to sexually transmitted diseases, and pregnancy is possible if you're not in menopause. Buy condoms in a variety of styles and colors so you both can have fun choosing. If you are not menopausal, talk with your doctor about birth control. Diaphragms and IUD's are good choices if you cannot use any hormones.

When It's Time

Before you become intimate or sexual with a partner, and they will touch or see your body, it's good to have done the work described earlier in the book, especially the mirror processes, so that you are comfortable with how your body is now. You may never feel exactly like you did before cancer; however, you are a beautiful, desirable, sexy woman with or without your original breasts.

I believe that the breast cancer experience is an opportunity for you to heal any wounds to your femininity and sexuality and to feel more powerful and desirable than before. Love and celebrate all of you, and pamper that beautiful body of yours. Shop for a pair of heels that make your legs look incredible. Put on your sexiest underwear, and open that yummy-smelling lotion you got for your birthday.

You are a beautiful, desirable, sexy woman with or without your original breasts

You don't have to wait for someone else's approval. When you feel desirable and attractive, it shows.

"Caroline says: "I do have body issues as far as the loss of my breast is concerned. However, my partner is not bothered about the mastectomy side and makes much of my remaining breast!"

For me, I've come to love my breasts and to value my scars. I think they make me much sexier, in fact. The breast with surgeries and radiation doesn't respond in the same way as the other, and it has become a point of discussion with my partner.

It's possible you may need some professional guidance to get you to this point. If you feel challenged by your self-image, go to support groups or see a therapist or coach. Until you see yourself as beautiful and desirable, it will be difficult for your partners to see you that way.

Your partner will pick up on your anxieties, so do whatever it takes to relax. Set the tone with candlelight and soft music. Leave your lingerie on if it makes you more comfortable. Are you still wearing a wig? If so, consider using it for role-playing: "Would you like me to be a redhead or a blonde tonight?" Most of all, take your time with long, thoughtful foreplay. Slow your partner down if you have to, but chances are you'll be enjoying each other so much that this won't be an issue. One way a woman can help the situation is to have an orgasm before intercourse or penetration. It will be much more enjoyable for you because you will be relaxed and lubricated, and the tissues will be more supple.

Staying Active

Whether or not you're in a relationship, adopt the "use it or lose it" approach. Put sex into your schedule the way you would with exercise. I do my sexercises and make sure to have regular orgasms, whether through sex with a partner or through self-pleasure with a vibrator or other toys.

If you don't have a partner or have sex regularly, then try other means of stimulation that you can use on a regular basis.

If you don't have a shop nearby or don't feel comfortable going to one, there are some wonderful online stores (Good Vibrations, A Woman's Touch, others). The benefit to going to a store is that you can speak with the staff there to ask questions. Look on my website (**www.sexyaftercancer. com**) for product reviews and recommendations.

For Younger Women with Breast Cancer

Research at Indiana University shows that young women who have had breast cancer also have sexual issues. These include genital pain, vaginal dryness, premature menopause, fertility problems, fatigue, and low libido, which results in trouble becoming aroused, desire and orgasm. Unwilling to live without having a sex life, most of them expressed interest in using lubricants and massage oils to help with pain and dryness. More than half were curious about vibrators and dildos, and a third would play sex games.

with many more years to live with this, finding ways to come back to sexual functioning and pleasure is a high priority

The women in the study also indicated that they would be comfortable purchasing sexual enhancement products at in-home parties or at their breast cancer support groups, and less comfortable using adult websites or book stores.

(Source: "Young Female Breast Cancer Survivors: their sexual function and interest in sexual enhancement products and services," published 11/4/08 in the journal Cancer Nursing)

About 12-15% of cancer diagnoses are in women between the ages of 20-35, which is significant. With many more years to live with this, finding ways to come back to sexual functioning and pleasure is a high priority. Fertility can also be an issue. See the chapter on fertility and family planning for more on this.

Work out those Pelvic Floor Muscles

See the Sexercise in chapter 13 for information about strengthening your pelvic floor muscles and other exercises to do to keep "in shape."

Being on the cancer journey, we know how short life is, so we need to make the most of every moment. Surviving cancer can make us better lovers because we appreciate so much more now. Single guys (and women if that's your preference) should feel lucky to date us! You have had breast cancer. Life goes on. You are not going to reverse what happened, but there is a future for you and sex should be a large part of that.

Take a good look at yourself and see how beautiful you really are. Get past your inhibitions and buy a couple of toys. Find the right partner, and don't waste your time with those who can't handle your situation. Be brave and take chances. You have your whole life ahead of you. Make it fabulous!

17

CANCER, FERTILITY AND FAMILY PLANNING

What if you received your diagnosis before having children?

What if you have a child or children and would like to have more?

What if you're not sure about having children but want to have the option?

you may suddenly find yourself menopausal

If you are in any of these situations, it's important to talk with your doctors before you begin your treatment. Depending on the treatment you have, you may suddenly find yourself menopausal. Depending on your age, which drugs you're given and your own body's unique response, this may be temporary or permanent. You may want to harvest eggs prior to treatment. It's wise to explore all the possibilities and make the best preparations you can. There are many variables, so please discuss this with your doctor.

I am not advocating one option or another. And please remember that this is not medical advice in any way. This information is not intended to influence your medical treatment decisions in any way, simply to raise your awareness to this important issue.

According to breastcancer.org, this is what is now known:

- Early menopause brought on by chemotherapy may be temporary. In other words, your menstrual periods may stop and then start again after chemotherapy is over. It can take a few months or as long as a year or more for your periods to return.

- Periods don't always mean fertility. Even if your periods start after treatment, your fertility may be uncertain. You may need to see a fertility expert to help you find out if you're actually fertile.

- Women who get relatively high overall doses of chemotherapy may be more likely to be infertile after treatment than women on lower-dose regimens.

- Chemotherapy medicines are usually given in combination, not each one by itself. When used in combination, the medicines' effect on fertility may be different. It's also important to know that the same medicine may be given in different doses in different combinations.

- Some women who have normal periods after chemotherapy may be able to get pregnant with no difficulty while others may have trouble getting pregnant. This is because chemotherapy can damage the immature eggs in the ovaries.

- When your periods return after chemotherapy, it means that some eggs are maturing. But you may have fewer eggs available than before chemotherapy.

- Because chemotherapy may cause birth defects, doctors advise using birth control -- but not birth control pills -- throughout chemotherapy so you don't become pregnant during treatment.

- It's important to wait at least 6 months (or longer) to get pregnant after chemotherapy ends. You don't want to get pregnant with an egg that was damaged by chemotherapy.

- After chemotherapy, fertility may be short-lived. This means that even women whose periods start again after chemotherapy are at some risk of early menopause.

In addition to the medical journey associated with breast cancer, there's the emotional journey. It can be a real roller coaster, an "e-ticket ride." My story is an example.

I was young and single when I was diagnosed. I always thought that the picture of my life would be driving around a big SUV filled with puppies and babies, living in a house with a white picket fence, the happy and tranquil domestic family scene. That's not how it turned out for me. Instead, when I received my diagnosis on my 37th birthday, I was single and childless.

it can be a real roller coaster

I was really fortunate to have my diagnosis come at a very early stage. The tumor was too small to check for estrogen receptors and I had no positive lymph nodes, so I chose to have radiation therapy as the only treatment following my two surgeries. I knew that later, if needed, chemo and hormonal therapy were options.

Just before I had my second surgery, I met my sweetheart. I was madly in love and the love and sexual intimacy we shared were a big part of my healing journey. Our sexual life fulfilled me and helped me stay sane in many ways. One day during my radiation protocol, we were making love and the condom broke.... You guessed it. Six weeks later I discovered that I was pregnant. It was a very mixed emotional experience for me. The potential of new life, in the midst of the heartbreak of breast cancer, was thrilling to me. At the same time, I didn't know if I was out of the woods.

I had an appointment with my gynecologist to confirm the home pregnancy test. Yes indeed, I was pregnant. And the doctor was wildly upset and told me that I should not be pregnant, then or ever. He said that if there were any cancer cells floating around in my body, the exponential hormonal production of pregnancy would probably have any lurking cancer cells grow like weeds, putting both me and the baby at great risk. He also said that because my body was depleted from surgeries and radiation, it might be a difficult pregnancy and a high likelihood that the baby would be born with "problems", unspecified. He said I needed to have a therapeutic abortion immediately.

I was terrified and heart broken. This on top of everything else nearly did me in. We went home to think about it overnight, but not before the appointment for the next day was made.

After a sleepless night, we decided to have the abortion. It happened that day. My sweetie held my hand throughout and I sobbed. I felt such deep grief, sadness and loss. It was more than the loss of the fetus – it felt like the loss of my fertility, the loss of the possibility of ever having a baby, and the loss of my hope. This was definitely the low point of my cancer journey so far.

I was in psychotherapy at this point, with someone whose specialty was people with life-threatening diseases. When I went for my next session with her, I told her about the pregnancy and abortion. It had all happened so quickly, I was reeling from it all. She was surprised at my news and asked what I wanted. I said what I wanted was the possibility of having a baby one day if my relationship stayed strong and our love was strong and healthy, and that I was healthy.

She asked if I would feel unfulfilled if I never had a child. Up until then, I had always just assumed that I would have at least one child. Now it felt like that choice had been taken away and I didn't get to vote. Underneath the anger and fear, I came face-to-face with the opportunity to step up and take responsibility for my life, on my terms. This was a huge turning point for me. I was able to grieve my losses and choose how I wanted to live my life and discover what was important to me and what was not so important.

Fast-forward two years, and my sweetie and I married. The one unresolved issue when we married was whether we would have a child or not. I prayed, trusted, surrendered to divine will, and took a leap of faith to marry a man who wasn't certain that he wanted more children (he had one from a previous marriage).

it felt like that choice had been taken away and I didn't get to vote

We sat in the uncertainty for many months. Then we participated in a workshop (one of the Love, Intimacy and Sexuality series). Before the workshop began we had a conversation about what we wanted to learn and how we wanted to grow from the experience. My focus was to get clear whether we'd have a child or not. I was tired of sitting on the fence. I knew I'd find my peace no matter what the choice. By the end of workshop, we knew without a doubt that we wanted to have a child. I was elated and terrified. I knew what my doctor thought and advised, and I knew what I wanted and needed to feel fulfilled as a woman. I was willing to take the risks and the responsibility for the consequences of my choices.

> *the journey was filled with roadblocks, detours and heartache, and it was worth it*

We began trying to get pregnant in earnest, which meant lots of intercourse, especially around ovulation. I got pregnant almost immediately and just as quickly I miscarried. That happened twice in rapid succession. I had no idea whether this was a result of the cancer treatments, my age (I was now 40) or something else. It was stressful beyond belief. I was taking my vaginal temperature every morning upon awakening to determine when I was ovulating. Each time we made love, I lay with my feet propped up overhead so that the sperm would stay inside me longer and travel to the egg easier without having to defy gravity. A friend gave me a fertility talisman. We created a sacred ritual to invite the baby into my womb and our lives. You name it, we tried it.

After 6 months, I got pregnant again. Six weeks passed, then 10, and finally the first trimester. Cautiously optimistic, we had amniocentesis to determine the health of the fetus. All looked fine. The pregnancy continued and my daughter was born just before my 41st birthday. She was truly a miracle. That was 19 years ago!

My story had a happy ending, and I'm thankful every day that I followed my heart and soul's longing and had a healthy baby. The journey was filled with roadblocks, detours and heartache, and it was worth it. I'd do it again.

All this is to say that I understand what this part of the cancer journey can be like. It can be heart wrenching and also very empowering. It's definitely an emotional and physical roller coaster.

If this is part of your journey, my wish for you is that you consult with your doctors, and that you follow your heart and your dreams. I trust that you will make the best choices for you and that you will experience the best outcome for you as well. Remember that your doctor's job is to keep you alive at all costs, and that often means they don't consider the quality of your life to be as important as you do. If I could wave my magic wand and empower you to trust yourself completely and look deeply into what really matters for you about having children, I would do that.

You can consider me your fairy godmother if that works for you!

I wish you blessings with this!

18

GOING FORWARD

We've covered a lot of territory in this book! Some of it may be familiar to you or may not apply to you, and much of it is probably new. How do you take what appeals to you and integrate it into your life? Receiving so much information can be a bit daunting, so take a deep breath and relax, and another deep breath. All of this is meant to inspire you and give you some ideas and possibilities for going forward from this point in your life. You get to decide what to use, when to use it and how to do it, and remember that there's no right or wrong way to do it, only your way.

> *The opportunity offered in this book is to transform yourself, to literally re-create yourself*

Many of the exercises and processes are simple, like doing nice things for yourself. Others, like the mirror practices take more time. And the practices related to working with your mind and subconscious thoughts, require a commitment, some discipline and consistency.

The opportunity offered in this book is to transform yourself, to literally re-create yourself. It can be done ~ I'm the poster girl for that ~ and it takes commitment, devotion, time and persistence, along with faith, trust and love.

You may be one of the rare people who makes a decision and does whatever it takes to reach your goal, no matter what. If that's you, Brava! I applaud you!

Or you may think that things will never change, and you'll bump along feeling resigned or depressed about what can happen for you.

Most of us fall somewhere between those two places: We want to change our lives and are committed to it, and we need some help and support along the way. We need the feedback that we're going in the right direction and that all is progressing as it should.

Part of my purpose is to be your cheerleader for what's possible, and to offer hope, inspiration and encouragement for living your life the way you want to. Sometimes when we make changes, it is smooth sailing and sometimes there's resistance. And the resistance can come from surprising places – not only from our inner critics and bullies, but also from people in our lives who want us to stay just as we were.

One of the ironies of growth is that is also invites those around us to grow. This can evoke resistance. Remember that this resistance isn't about you, it's about them. Keep your own intentions clear and keep going. You may already have experienced changes in your relationships as a result of your diagnosis – cancer can be a disease of separation and some people simply can't be around it, while others can. It's similar with growth – some people welcome growth and some resist it. A little trick that I find useful when someone doesn't like what I'm doing is to say to myself, "Thank you for sharing, so and so." And then I continue with my growth.

It also helps me to remember that what others think of what I'm doing is about them, not me – it's literally none of my business what they think of me! He, he, he...

> how to grow in your femininity, intimacy, sexuality and relationships? Your journey has already begun!

So, how to grow in your femininity, intimacy, sexuality and relationships? You've already taken the first steps by reading this book! Your interest in and intention to heal and grow are the foundation pieces. Your journey has already begun!

It's helpful to know that baby steps are enough, especially if you continue to take them, at your own pace. Your commitment is the most important part to making changes.

> *"Until one is committed, there is hesitancy, the chance to draw back-- Concerning all acts of initiative (and creation), there is one elementary truth the ignorance of which kills countless ideas and splendid plans: that the moment one definitely commits oneself, then Providence moves too. All sorts of things occur to help one that would never otherwise have occurred. A whole stream of events issues from the decision, raising in one's favor all manner of unforeseen incidents and meetings and material assistance, which [no woman] could have dreamed would have come [her] way. Whatever you can do, or dream you can do, begin it. Boldness has genius, power, and magic in it. Begin it now."*
>
> *~ **W.H. Murray** ~*

First, set up your environment to support your growth and evolution. By this I mean all aspects of your environment from your physical surroundings, who you spend time with, and what you eat, read and listen to. If a beautiful and tranquil environment will support you, do things like buying yourself beautiful flowers and having them in your home.

take an inventory of the areas of your life and make any changes that are more aligned with who you are now, what's important to you and what's not

Get rid of clutter and things that you no longer use or wear or that don't work. If you wear make-up, sort through it and toss the old tubes of lipstick that are drying up, the bits of eye shadow that are flaky, the old foundation.

Go through your closet and get rid of things you haven't worn for a year or that no longer fit. You can even have a clothing swap party with friends and give things to each other.

Eat food that supports your health and well-being. Drink plenty of water. Get enough sleep. Exercise.

If there are people in your life that aren't positive and supportive, consider spending less time with them. We are highly influenced by what others think, feel, say and do, and if it drags you down, perhaps now is a time to surround yourself with more positive people.

You get the idea – take an inventory of the areas of your life and make any changes that are more aligned with who you are now, what's important to you and what's not.

Some of these areas are:

- Your home

- Your work

- Spiritual practice

- Diet and exercise or fitness

- Friends and family

- Your thoughts

- What you read, watch and hear (TV, radio, books, movies, music, etc)

- How you spend your free time

Once your environment is the way you want it to be, or you are in that process, it will support your healing, your growth and awakening. Then you can do the other parts.

The journey of awakening your femininity and sexuality begins with the inner work. My suggestion is that you begin there, even if you already love yourself. We can all love ourselves more, so use these processes and exercises often, knowing that each time you do, you can deepen your experiences. People who are at peace with and love themselves

> *The journey of awakening your femininity and sexuality begins with the inner work*

attract others to them magnetically. There are no short cuts with this, so take as much time as you need.

It can be very helpful to keep a journal of what you're doing and your thoughts, feelings and experiences as you go along. Not only can you capture your experiences in a journal, but you can also see your growth and progress over time.

Once you are feeling more positive about yourself and your desirability and lovability, you have a good foundation for expanding your capacities for intimacy and sexuality. Both intimacy and sexuality arise from the foundation of self-acceptance and self-love. As you begin to explore your sexuality, be gentle and compassionate with yourself. Your body is different now and it's helpful to be curious about it. See if you can have the attitude and context of "beginner's mind."

Beginner's mind is operating as if what you're doing is for the very first time. It's all new and unknown and filled with possibilities. If you have no expectations, it's impossible to be disappointed. This may be easier said than done; however, reminding yourself to "come from" beginner's mind can be the source of much pleasure and learning.

There's no wrong way to do this. What's important is to do it your way. No one can tell you how to do what you're doing or how it should feel, or how quickly or slowly to go. Trust yourself and your inner knowing. Ask yourself for guidance, and listen for what comes to you. It may come as an intuition or knowing, as a question, or in a dream or as you write in your journal.

have the attitude and context of beginner's mind

You might choose to experiment with one process each week. Whether or not you have a partner, make an agreement to have a date night each week. Put it in your calendar so that nothing interferes with the time you have set aside. This is your time to devote to femininity, intimacy and sexuality, alone or with another.

If you need help with this, there are many sources of help. You have this book. You can go to my website (**www. sexyaftercancer.com**) and download many of the meditations and visualizations. There are also many articles there, and a resource section with many links to websites, book lists and other helpful resources.

this is your time to devote to femininity, intimacy and sexuality, alone or with another

You can start a support group with others who are on this journey. Sometimes the support of a group is useful – to have a place to share what's happening, compare notes, and keep each other on track and cheer each other up as you go along, works well for some people.

Here's what I know: There are many wonderful resources available, from caring and compassionate health care professionals to how-to books. I liken those resources to helping you to understand what chocolate tastes like – wonderful descriptions. And descriptions aren't the same as tasting chocolate. The difference with Sexy After Cancer is that we offer the tastes of chocolate. It's an entirely different experience than getting advice or reading about it. We are committed to helping you live a robust life that includes a happy, healthy and satisfying intimate and sexual life.

descriptions aren't the same as tasting chocolate

So we offer opportunities for you to come and have some chocolates.

You can attend one of my retreats. I offer a series of retreats for women with breast cancer, for couples, and for partners of women with breast cancer. You can find more information about these, as well as a schedule, at **www. sexyaftercancer.com/retreats**.

I also work with people individually, on the phone, via Skype and in person. This support is available in a number of formats: a series of hour-long sessions or a personal retreat where you come work with me for an entire day or more. This is available for individuals and for couples. Go to my website for more information.

most of us weren't raised believing that we are sexy, sexual beings

I am also conducting an ongoing research panel for breast cancer and femininity, intimacy and sexuality. This is a series of periodic surveys, focus groups, interviews and discussions. If you'd like to participate in this, go to the website to sign up.

You can also visit our Facebook page at **http://tinyurl. com/7am574r** for information, discussions, connections and resources.

I travel around the country and give talks and workshops. If you have a group and would like me to come and give a presentation, I welcome that. Go to the website for information and schedules.

I write in my blog regularly about various related topics, and there is a lively discussion there – **www.sexyaftercancer.com/blog**.

Re-creating yourself as a beautiful, desirable, sexy woman is one of the greatest opportunities of your life. Most of us weren't raised believing that we are sexy, sexual beings. Many women live their lives without having these experiences.

For those of us who are on the cancer journey, our very essence as feminine, sexy desirable women is shaken. We come face to face with our mortality, the choice to live and thrive, and to understand and accept who we are now as a result of this diagnosis and treatments.

In my view, this is one of the gifts of cancer – the opportunity to completely re-create ourselves. When we realize that this isn't a dress rehearsal and that life is very precious, it's also possible to realize the extraordinary opportunity we have to make choices about who we are and how we want to live our lives, for the rest of our lives.

My deepest wish for you is that you know absolutely that you are magnificent, that you are sexy, that you are desirable and that getting to know yourself at these deepest levels of your essence is the key to living an extraordinary life. You now have the freedom to choose.

Choose wisely and choose well, and enjoy the journey!

APPENDIX

1. Legal documents for surgery

I am not a legal professional, so please consult one for advice on these matters. You will be asked to sign documents, so it's wise to be prepared.

You will discuss your procedure/s with your physician prior to surgery. Sometimes they see things differently during the procedure than what is provided through the diagnostics. For example, a tumor my be larger than thought, or there may be more than one tumor. In this situation, the doctor may talk with you about how that will be handled during surgery, when you are under anesthesia and unable to make a decision.

My suggestion is that after discussing all of this with your doctor, you have a conversation with the person who will accompany you to surgery. Talk with them about the possibilities and what you'd like to have happen in those events. This person can then act as your advocate if they have been given Durable Power of Attorney for Healthcare.

a. Informed consent form

Prior to surgery, you will receive a careful explanation of the procedure, its purpose, any risks, and the expected outcome. You may also be asked to sign an "informed consent" form, which states in detail that you understand everything involved with your surgery. You should read through the consent carefully before signing it. If you have any questions or need more information, ask your physician.

b. Durable Power of Attorney for Healthcare

Durable Power of Attorney for Healthcare--This document designates another person to make healthcare decisions if the patient is not able to make them. This designated person can be a family member or friend, whoever you choose. In case of a decision that needs to be made while you are in surgery, this document allows this person to make decisions on your behalf.

NOTE: this document must be notarized, so you need to prepare it before you go into the hospital for surgery.

c. Insurance information

After diagnosis and if surgery is recommended, most insurance companies require "precertification" from the physician's office before allowing a patient to undergo the procedure. Please check with your insurance carrier on the appropriate steps to take. Some insurance companies also require patients to pay a co-payment for the hospital stay.

ACKNOWLEDGEMENTS

Like raising a child, it has taken a village to birth this book and the work of transformation for women with breast cancer.

Eileen Barker, God spoke to me through you and I listened. That was the genesis of this ~ thank you!

Vicki Landes graciously allowed me to work with her breast cancer support groups and test out some of these ideas. Thank you for your vision, your support and for providing some of my "guinea pigs/angels".

The women participants in the Kaiser Permanente support groups gave me honest feedback on this work and about what they needed and wanted. This has been a huge help in shaping it.

Some of my brilliant teachers and mentors ~ Stan Dale (in memoriam) and the Human Awareness Institute, Desda Zuckerman and Core Individuation, Michael Margolis and Get Storied, David Neagle and Life is Now, Swami Satchidananda (in memoriam) and the IntegSral Yoga Institute, Dean Ornish and Preventive Medicine Research Institute, Rachel Naomi Remen, Michael Lerner and

Commonweal, Saniel and Linda Groves Bonder ~ all have inspired me in various ways to follow my dream and my passion.

Chas August, my longtime friend, colleague and collaborator, I'm so thrilled to be on this part of the journey with you.

All the physicians, health care professionals, therapists, women on the breast cancer journey have been so generous with your time, information and requests.

Jan Adrian and the Board of Healing Journeys have seen the potential for this work from the beginning and have sponsored me as I spread my wings to fly.

My production team ~ Ana Hillis at Repurpose for Profit, Sandee Whalen at SINC Communications, Karen Frank at The Linguistic Alchemist, Janet Foust the Social Media Queen ~ you are all Rock Stars!

Ron Morgan, my sweetheart and life partner, has been patient, generous, loving and holding my hand as I leap into the unknown world of following this passion. Thank you, Sweetheart!

ABOUT THE AUTHOR

Barbara Musser had breast cancer in 1989, as a young single woman. She married and had a child after treatment. As a sex educator and workshop facilitator for 20+ years, she has supported many women and their partners and families along the journey; interviewed hundreds of women about their experiences and needs; worked with support groups on the subject of sexuality and intimacy; presented to tumor boards and interviewed many surgeons, plastic surgeons and oncologists about the subject.

Barbara is a frequent speaker on sexuality and intimacy. She is a member of the American Association of Sexuality Educators, Counselors and Therapists and the International Society for the Study of Women's Sexual Health.

You can book Barbara for a speaking engagement or workshop by going to her at **http://www.sexyaftercancer.com**

You can also contact her by:

- email at info@sexyaftercancer.com

- or by phone at (901) 300-0660